D1384062

BIG3MMD: History's Ambidextrous and the Benefits of Mirror Movement Development covers the history, science, and benefits of mirror movement development (MMD). It is the world's first modern *biscriptal* book, written in both traditional and mirrored script.

Who are the "Big Three" in *BIG3MMD*? They are *Leonardo da Vinci, Benjamin Franklin,* and *Lord Robert Baden-Powell* – three of the most interesting, dual-dominant people of our millennium.

Dual-dominance – traditionally known as *ambidexterity* – can be developed by any average person through the practice of MMD for astounding benefits to both the body and brain.

Each of the historic MMD practitioners listed in *BIG3MMD* exercised and promoted dual-dominance as a springboard to greatness. For example, did you know that *Michelangelo* painted the Sistine Chapel with *both* hands? Or that *Mozart* composed music with the same approach? Even *Houdini* developed dual-dominance to become a better magician and encouraged the practice be taught to children!

Additional historic MMD practitioners and promoters include:

Ancient Greece	Plato	M.C. Escher
Thomas Jefferson	Hippocrates	Nikola Tesla
Mahatma Gandhi	Queen Victoria	Jimi Hendrix
James Garfield	Albert Einstein	Gordie Howe
Lewis Carroll	Easter Islanders	Mickey Mantle

The handedness of these historic figures, various of whom were polymaths, virtuosos, and renaissance men, is presented here in *BIG3MMD*.

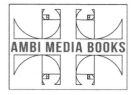
Written by Jim Houliston

Edited by Patricia Wallace
Editorial assistance by David Reisman, Richard Mogavero, and
   Maria Recupero English

Cover Image by J.P. Heston
Formatted by Saqib Arshad

ISBN: 979-8-9861525-0-9 (Paperback)
Library of Congress Control Number: 2022908218

First printing, May 2022
Philadelphia, PA 19104

www.AmbiLife.org

BIG3MMD

HISTORY'S AMBIDEXTROUS
AND THE BENEFITS OF
MIRROR MOVEMENT DEVELOPMENT

JIM HOULISTON

TABLE OF CONTENTS

HOW TO READ A BISCRIPTAL BOOK

BIG3MMD is the world's first modern *biscriptal* book. It is written in both traditional and mirrored script. To start the mirrored portion, simply flip the book over and begin at the 'back,' reading right-to-left. Both the traditional and mirrored versions include the same content. Your brain processes the mirrored version differently, though, growing your less-dominant brain hemisphere in the process.[1]

If you can read in the traditional direction, **mirror reading is achievable.** Like every new skill we learn, the ability to mirror read improves over time with practice. Remember, it took you time to learn reading in the traditional direction. Mirrored reading is no different. In fact, developmental studies show that cerebral symmetry is evident in children only *before* they learn traditional, unidirectional reading. This condition is balanced out through mirror reading and the general practice of MMD.[2]

Stick with this practice of mirror reading and your brain will thank you for the workout! You will learn more about the benefits of this exercise later in Chapter 5 on *Mirror Reading.*

WHAT IS MMD?

MMD is *mirror movement development.* Traditionally referred to as the practice of developing *ambidexterity* (aka *dual-dominance*), MMD is the mechanical design for optimal movement within our bilateral human body. It is practiced through focused development of the less-dominant side via mirrored movements. Examples of MMD include throwing with your less-dominant arm, kicking with your less-dominant foot, writing in mirrored direction with your less-dominant hand, reading in mirrored direction, and more.

The history, science, and benefits of MMD are presented here in *BIG3MMD*. The wide spectrum of historic ambidexters include three most notable: Lord Robert Baden-Powell, Benjamin Franklin, and Leonardo da Vinci. Additional information about MMD and stories from today's practitioners are available on my website, *AmbiLife.org*

DISCLAIMER

BIG3MMD came about after researching famous ambidextrous people from history. Various names appeared repeatedly in books and on websites. Those names and accounts are summarized here in *BIG3MMD*.

These famous people demonstrated a spectrum of handedness, from strongly mixed-handed – using different hands for different tasks (e.g. right-handed for tennis and left-handed for writing, like Bill Gates) – to highly ambidextrous. For many people, the word 'ambidextrous' has come to mean 'mixed-handed,' though the actual definition of ambidexterity means possessing an equal aptitude of either hand for all tasks. True ambidexterity has been quite rare, currently believed to be just one or two people in 1,000. Some scientists even argue that no one is *entirely* ambidextrous.[1]

It is even possible that some of these people were never ambidextrous at all, as in the cases of Albert Einstein and Benjamin Franklin – neither of whom ever wrote directly about their own handedness.[2] The people listed in *BIG3MMD* are all historic figures, so we cannot ask them today for clarification on their handedness. As a result, additional research and new information may produce another compelling edition of *BIG3MMD* in the future.

Regardless of the spectrum of *BIG3MMD's* historic ambidextrous, contemporary MMD practitioners show us that **ambidexterity (aka dual-dominance) can be developed by the average person through practice.** Learn more at *AmbiLife.org*.

INTRODUCTION

An *ambidexter* is someone who displays notable use of both hands, a trait commonly known as *ambidexterity*. The lives of many contemporary ambidexters show us that this skill is **not** something you are only born with, but can be developed through practice by any average person.[1]

Figure X.1 Average hands, like our bilateral sides, are mirror images

Mirror movement development (MMD) focuses on choosing to use your less-dominant side in mirrored direction for all activities. This lifestyle practice produces dual-dominance. 'Dual-dominance' is a more accurate term for the word 'ambidexterity,' which in Latin means, "right-handed on both sides"[2] or "two rights."[3] Since humans have both left *and* right lateral sides, 'ambidexterity' is not the most accurate word for describing the equal development of both mirrored sides of the human body. Cultures worldwide, though, have spent centuries understanding the practice of MMD as 'ambidexterity,' so this word is still used throughout *BIG3MMD* to describe dual-dominance, and vice versa.

One important part of the MMD lifestyle practice is having a *Can-Do* mindset of seeing our glasses as half-full. As a result, the commonly used word of 'non-dominant' has been replaced with

traumatic brain injury 54
twist-off bottle caps 49
type settings 33-34

U.S. Constitution 33
Udo-Udoma, Ebiye Jeremy 62, 73
unidextrous 47
uni-dominant 58
unilateral 46-48, 62
United States/U.S. 13, 14, 17, 19, 29, 33, 35, 63, 76
University of Alberta 46
University of Pennsylvania 30, 74
University of Southern California, San Diego 53

Valverde, Cat 74
Van Pelt-Dietrich Library 74
Vázquez Montaño, Daniel 74
violinist 17
visual 21, 54-55, 68
Visual Perception 68
visualization 55

walking 59-60, 65, 76
Wallace, Patricia 73
wallball 64
War on Drugs 76
watches 49
weight 12, 21, 45, 57, 61, 71
weird 62
West Chester University of Pennsylvania 75
West, Jim 36
White, Norman 66
Whitman, Walt 17
Whole Brain Power 49, 51, 61

Wilson, Sir Daniel 18
Wilson, Woodrow 19
women 51
workout 1, 51, 65
wrist 34
writing 3, 5, 8-9, 12-13, 17-18, 20, 22, 25, 27-31, 34-35, 37-42, 46, 52-53, 59-60, 67-68, 72-74
written language 18, 67

Yale University 34
Yoga 65, 69, 76

'less-dominant' when referring to handedness and footedness in *BIG3MMD*. A 'non-dominant' hand leaves little room for improvement. However, a 'less-dominant' hand is open to improvement through practice over time.

In the same spirit, the word 'CAN'T' has no place within the vocabulary of an average person when it comes to MMD. If the average person says, "I *can't* write or throw with my other hand," an appropriate response would be, "Okay, what is your *physical disability* then?" After looking confused, they may follow up with, "Well, nothing. I just don't know how to use my other hand that well." Which is okay! You are correct to say that *today*, but fluency develops over time with practice. MMD is all about the *practice* of working to develop your less-dominant side to become the dual-dominant person you are mechanically designed to be.

While MMD is nothing new to humanity, our contemporary *awareness* of it is somewhat novel. Science today is developing a better understanding of MMD and how it benefits both the mind and body. While there is ample scientific citation throughout *BIG3MMD,* the practice of MMD merits greater research, considering the practice's highly-attractive benefits.[4] The goal of *BIG3MMD* is to present accounts of famous, historic MMD practitioners and an understanding of the science and benefits of the practice through which readers can get a glimpse into the reality that dual-dominance can be developed today by any average person.

First and foremost, my interest is to see people inspired to practice MMD and experience the mental and physical benefits. My credentials for writing *BIG3MMD* lie not in being a doctor, historian, professor, researcher, or other academic professional, but rather in the experience of being a 10+ year practitioner of MMD whose life has been dramatically changed by it. So, wherever you find citation lacking, please remember the words of my fellow MMD practitioner, the informally schooled, Leonardo da Vinci:[5] *"Though I may not, like them (the 'experts'), be able to quote other authors, I shall rely on that which is much greater and more worthy: on experience, the mistress of their Masters."*[6]

My personal relationship with MMD began inadvertently 15 years ago as a way to physically rehabilitate my body from 10 years of skateboarding, which was done entirely using my dominant side. Frequent visits to chiropractors didn't solve my body alignment problems, so I reluctantly quit the sport. One year later, in 2007, I had the idea to try *switch-stance* skating. Switch-stance means performing the activity from your less-dominant side (aka mirrored). Up to this moment, I did everything in life exclusively right-handed and right-footed, so switching my stance was extremely challenging. I persisted though and guess what? This lifestyle practice notably *realigned my body* after just four years!

Shortly after, I returned to trying my regular stance in skateboarding again. I was quite nervous though as I did not want to reinjure myself. Surprisingly, I found that I was immediately able to perform *new* regular-stance tricks – thanks to a beautiful concept known as *manual transfer learning.*[7] I then wondered, "What would happen to my body if I learned *everything* switch?" From that moment, I gradually worked to learn everything switch-stance. This is the lifestyle practice of mirror movement development (MMD).

Today, after a cumulative 10+ years of practicing MMD, I started *AmbiLife.org* to introduce others to the lifestyle. MMD has not only astronomically changed my life, but also the lives of other practitioners I know.

There are people today reading this book who want to physically and mentally feel as good as I do and are willing to adopt the MMD

observation 14, 27, 39, 40
observer 38
Old Forge, Pennsylvania 75
Olympic Handball player 62
Opificio delle Pietre Dure 37
optimal 3, 64, 69, 71
order 26, 31, 60
Ottomans 13
Oxford University 34
oxygen 50

painter 41
painting 23, 27, 33, 37
Palmer, Dr. Richard 46
Parkway Central Library of Philadelphia 38
patients 15, 54, 68
peak performance 71
Persia 13
Petition of the Left Hand 29-30, 34
phantom limb pain 53
Philadelphia 14, 17, 34, 36, 52, 74-75
philosopher 15, 29
physical disability 8
ping pong dancing 59, 64, 76
Plato 15
Pliny 13
polymath 15, 18, 27, 29, 36-37, 39-40, 63, 71-72
postural problems 64
posture 40, 50, 59
practice 1-2, 7-8, 12-13, 15, 26, 31, 35, 37-38, 40, 43, 46-47, 50, 62, 68, 71
pregnenolone 52
Princeton University 19

professor 14, 19, 33-34, 46, 68
progesterone 52
pronation muscles 49
Proposals Relating to the Education of Youth 30
Psychology 33, 68

Queen Victoria 14, 18-19, 25

rail walking 59-60, 63, 76
Ramachandran, Dr. V.S. 53, 74
Raphael 38
reaction time 57-58
Reade, Charles 14
reading 1, 3, 9, 34-35, 39, 42-43, 46, 53, 55, 67-70, 74
reading-in-a-mirror technique 70
realignment 42, 71
Recupero English, Maria 73
regular-stance 9
rehabilitation 34, 37, 47, 66, 71, 76
Reisman, David 73
Renaissance 16, 18, 23, 37-38
research 5, 37, 46, 51, 61, 68-69, 74
researcher 8, 68
Reyes, Sebastian 74
Rhombicuboctahedron 38
right hand 5, 7, 9, 11, 16, 20-22, 27, 29, 32-33, 37, 39, 49, 51-53, 67, 73
Right Hand, Left Hand 33
right-brain 20, 49, 51, 53, 69
right-handedness 30, 51

lifestyle to get there. *BIG3MMD* is dedicated to those up-and-coming MMD practitioners. While the stories of contemporary MMD practitioners merit writing a future book, let's first start with the stories of our historic, world-changing MMD practitioners...

handwriting 17, 37, 39, 40-42, 52, 59-60

Harvard University 34

hemisphere 1, 20, 29, 46, 49, 49

Hemispheric Recognition of Language 52

Hendrix, Jimi 14, 22

Herodotus 13

high-precision balance 57, 60, 71

hip 65

hippocampi 52

hippocampus 51

Hippocrates 14-15

history 34, 61, 72

Houdini, Harry 14, 19-20

Houliston, Jim 75

Howe, Gordie 65

human 3, 7, 12, 22-23, 26, 36, 38-41

Huntington's patients 68

ice hockey 65

imagination 20, 55

imbalances 64

Indiana Jones 23

injury 54, 65

inversions 59, 64, 76

inverted writing 12-13, 23, 34, 37, 41-42, 59

iPhone 68

Irigoyen, Diego 41, 51, 61, 73

Jackson, John 26

Japan, 13

jeans 48

Jefferson, Thomas 17, 34-35

Jenga 59

Jensen, Luke 65

Jessurun de Mesquita, Samuel 21

Jones, Adam 73

Josephus 13

juggling 64

Justin 13

Kenya, Nyeri 29

Kids 49, 68

Ko, Dr. Kathryn 63, 73

ladies 49

Landseer, Edwin Henry 19

language 19, 46, 51, 52, 67

Latin 7, 19

Latin America 76

Lavery, Michael J. 49, 51, 60-61, 53, 73

learn 1, 6, 9, 12, 28, 49, 50

left arm 54

left hand 11, 16-17, 20-22, 27-30, 32-33, 52

left side 48-49, 54, 65

left-brain 49, 51-52

Left-hand writing by soldiers 17

left-handed 5, 11, 19, 21-22, 28, 30, 33-34, 37, 51, 53, 73

less-dominant 1, 3, 7-9, 14, 17, 35, 39-40, 48-49, 51, 53, 58, 62, 65-66, 69, 72

lifestyle 7, 9, 48, 71-72

ligaments 38, 64

longboarding 62, 76

longevity 13, 57, 64-65, 71

looking-glass letters 18

luminaries 15, 36-37, 71-72

machine 38, 45, 49, 51, 64, 73

CHAPTER 1

History's Spectrum of MMD

Nothing in the bilateral, mechanical design of the average human body can explain our overwhelming, global preference for developing the right hand over the left.[1] In fact, nearly all bilateral species under the sun have an even 50/50 split in handedness.[2] Humans are the *only* bilateral species with a drastic split – nearly 90% still favoring the right hand over the left. As a result, much of our human-designed world is asymmetric.[3] Everything from power tools to zippers and can openers are made exclusively for use by the right hand. This can explain how the left-handed must practice some mixed-handed degree of ambidexterity. If you need proof, grab a can of tuna and try using your left hand to open it.

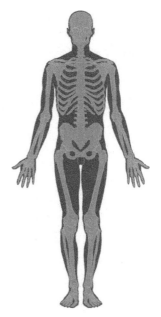

Figure 1.1: Humans are mechanically designed for symmetric movement

Could it be that the timeless practice of MMD is actually the more practical, intuitive, and holistic approach to body mechanics and human development? Considering the bilaterally symmetric design of an average human skeleton, exterior sensory features (eyes, ears, hands, feet, etc.), and weight distribution of the entire organic system, what can be accomplished by one side of our body, can be accomplished by the other side *equally* – if taught.[4]

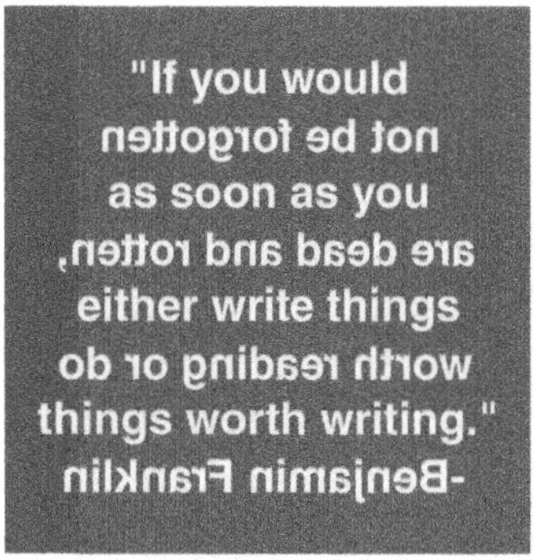

"If you would not be forgotten as soon as you are dead and rotten, either write things worth reading or do things worth writing." -Benjamin Franklin

Figure 1.2: Modern example of boustrophedon: the handwriting style of ancient Greece

Most young children instinctively practice MMD.[5] As they learn to kick, throw, reach, and turn to grab objects, both sides of the body engage. If their development is not hindered, some children begin writing in mirrored and even inverted direction with both hands.[6] Leonardo da Vinci, as we shall see, practiced this skill his entire life.

Let's take a look at various civilizations and cultures who practiced MMD throughout history:

The **ancient Greeks** were one of the most advanced civilizations our world has ever known, making never-before-seen advancements in architecture, medicine, civic organization, mathematics, philosophy, astronomy, and more.[7] While carving script onto stone walls between the 12th and 5th centuries BCE,[8] ancient Greeks displayed dual-dominance in their biscriptal writing style known as *boustrophedon* – a word that means, "Like the ox plowing at a turn."[9] Boustrophedon writing flows in one direction, then continues the next line in the opposite direction, creating mirrored script (see

body realignment 42, 71
book 1-2, 5, 9, 25-26
Boston 14
boustrophedon 12, 37
Boy Scouts 23-28, 74
brain 1, 13, 15, 17, 20-21, 33, 40, 41-42, 45-54, 57-58, 61-63, 68-69, 71-73
British 23-25, 63
Broca's area 52-53
broke 17, 34
Brownsea Island 25
Butler, Katie 74
butterflies 25

calligraphy 13-14, 18
camera obscura 40
can openers 11, 49
CAN'T 8
Can-Do mindset 7
car 48, 64, 71
caregivers 15
CBS 61
Celsus 16
Center for Brain and Cognition 53
century 13, 15-16, 23, 25, 40
cerebellum 50
cerebral cortex 50-51
chalk art 59, 76
Chaplin, Dr. Joyce 34
chemical reactions 52
chemistry 27
childhood 21, 31, 54, 73
children 1, 12, 19, 32, 49, 71
chiropractor 9, 60, 66
Church-related Anxiety Disorder (C-RAD) 76

Clocks 49
Codex Leicester 42, 89
cognitive 68
color perspective 39
communication 20, 26, 50, 58, 75
computer mice 49
Constitution 33
coordination 57, 65
corkscrews 49
corpus callosum 20, 50-51
cortex 69
Creative Brain Training 41, 51, 61
creativity 41, 57, 63
credit card machines 49
cross-hemispheric communication 58
culture 7, 12-14, 26, 33, 48, 67
cycling 65

Da Vinci, Leonardo 3, 9, 12-14, 23, 36-42, 59, 68
Dante 38
Dawson College of Montreal, Canada 68
Declaration of Independence 33
definitiveness 39
dentate gyrus 52
design 3, 11-12, 38, 42, 48, 71, 72
desks 49
devil 22
DHEA 52
direction 3, 7, 12, 33-34, 46, 53, 67
directionality 67
discipline 15, 24, 27, 40-41, 48, 63
dislocated hand 37
doctors 14

INDEX

Figure 1.2). Switching hands between lines is the ideal way to write boustrophedon. Try it with a simple paragraph. This activity, like all MMD, equally exercises both sides of the brain and body.[10]

Ancient historians like Josephus, Pliny, Justin, and Herodotus wrote of the **Scythians**: a flourishing civilization known for their physical longevity, strength, and military success. It is recorded that the Scythian culture legally instituted the practice of MMD in all their activities.[11]

Figure 1.3: Rongorongo: the dual-dominant writing style of the Easter Islanders

As early as the 17th century, the **Easter Islanders** had their own dual-dominant, biscriptal writing style with *rongorongo.*[12] It was similar to boustrophedon, but with an additional element: *inverted* alternating lines. Two centuries earlier, on the other side of the world, Leonardo da Vinci was filling his own personal notebooks with, both, mirrored and inverted writing.[13]

The 18th-century **Ottomans** practiced MMD through their mystical, mirrored calligraphy.[14]

The late 19th century was a notable time for MMD in the world, particularly in **Great Britain, Japan, Persia,** and **the United States.**[15]

Figure 1.4: Symmetric calligraphy of the Ottoman Empire

Great Britain's Queen Victoria practiced MMD before the *Ambidextral Culture Society* was founded within her own country. Through this group, hundreds of people worked to develop dual-dominance, many of whom were doctors, surgeons, professors, and students.[16] One of these practitioners was the world-famous Lord Robert Baden-Powell.

The society influenced U.S. cities like Philadelphia[17] and Boston,[18] where school teachers demonstrated and instructed students to develop dual-dominance. Major League Baseball even had four ambidextrous pitchers during this time.[19] The era's Victorian novelist, Charles Reade, also wrote brashly that, "every child is even and either handed till some grown fool interferes and mutilates it."[20]

With additional practitioners like Plato, Hippocrates, Michelangelo, Mozart, Gandhi, Houdini, Hendrix, and more, you will see a variety of famous, historic people practicing a spectrum of MMD and experiencing robust benefits.

The "BIG 3" of Da Vinci, Franklin, and Baden-Powell are unique in their claims, observations, and practices relating to use of the less-dominant side. They also embodied a few notable

https://amblifeorg.files.wordpress.com/2022/03/dr-shelagh-robinson.jpg

5.3 – Creative Commons. Author: Basile Morin
https://commons.wikimedia.org/wiki/File:Ambigram_Body_Yoga,_mirror_symmetry.png

5.4 – Graphic by Jim Houliston
https://amblifeorg.files.wordpress.com/2022/03/screenshot_20220123-143232_gallery-e1647970072857.jpg

3.5 – Creative Commons. Author: Anatomography, Life Science Databases(LSDB). "Corpus Callosum."
https://commons.wikimedia.org/wiki/File:Corpus_callosum.png

3.6 – Public Domain
https://commons.wikimedia.org/wiki/File:Brain_Exercising.png

3.7 – Frontiers in Neurology. December 11, 2020. Editor: Nicola Smania.
https://www.frontiersin.org/articles/10.3389/fneur.2020.568261/full

3.8 – Photo by Jim Houliston
https://amblilifeorg.files.wordpress.com/2022/03/picsart_01-22-06.15.53.jpg

Chapter 4: The Benefits of MMD

4.1 – Creative Commons. Author: Nickbyrd
https://commons.wikimedia.org/wiki/File:Thinker_mri.jpg

4.2 – Photo by Brad Morris
https://amblilifeorg.files.wordpress.com/2022/03/screenshot_20220110-201903_gallery.jpg

4.3 – Public Domain
https://commons.wikimedia.org/wiki/File:Waist_measurement.jpg

4.4 – Public Domain
https://www.loc.gov/pictures/item/2002723319/

4.5 – Public Domain
https://commons.wikimedia.org/wiki/File:Gordie_Howe_Chex_card.jpg

Chapter 5: Mirror Reading

5.1 – Creative Commons. Author: Basile Morin
https://commons.wikimedia.org/wiki/File:Ambigram_Magic_Dream_-_mirror_symmetry_with_a_handheld_pattern_giving_a_reversed_shadow_on_a_blue_wall.jpg

5.2 – Photo by Shelagh Robinson

characteristics that may have been augmented by the brain-growing practice of MMD. Namely, they were:

- **Polymaths** who excelled in multiple, unrelated disciplines, ranging from science to art to math and music.
- **Luminaries** who inspired their fellow man and catalyzed large-scale cultural changes.
- **Naturephiles** who observed and cherished the created order.

Before we take a deeper dive into our "Big 3" and explore their notable standings on the MMD spectrum, here are some more honorable mentions:

The 4th-century BCE Greek philosopher, teacher, and founder of the first institution of higher education in the Western world,[21] **Plato**, was convinced that the limbs are naturally of equal strength, balance, and ability. He believed that dominant handedness was not part of our physical design, but rather a

Figure 1.5: Plato and Hippocrates praised and promoted dual-dominance

cultural impartation created by our caregivers' misguided habit of exclusivity.[22] Plato also praised the ancient Scythian archers for their ability to shoot equally from both sides of the body.[23]

The Father of Modern Medicine and Plato contemporary, **Hippocrates**, urged his patients to *"practice all the operations,*

15

performing them with each hand and with both together—for they are both alike—your object being ready to attain ability, grace, speed, painlessness, elegance and readiness. "[24]

Figure 1.6: Michelangelo used both hands to paint the Sistine Chapel

In the first century CE, **Celsus**, a Roman physician, encouraged dual-dominance for surgeons, saying they should be *"ready to use the left hand as well as the right."* [25]

Italian Renaissance genius, **Michelangelo**, painted his masterpiece, the Sistine Chapel ceiling, using both hands.[26] He also chose to portray Adam extending his left hand towards God.

Figure 1.7: Mozart composed music with both hands

Austrian classical composer, **Wolfgang Amadeus Mozart,** composed music with both his left and right hands.[27] Centuries later, his music would inspire

_Wincelslaus_Hollar,_out_of_the_Portland_Museum)_MET_DP8241
04.jpg

2.14 – Public Domain
https://commons.wikimedia.org/wiki/File:Da_Vinci_mirror_writing.jp
g

2.15 – Public Domain
https://commons.wikimedia.org/wiki/File:De_divina_proportione_-
_Illustration_05.jpg

2.16 – Graphic by Jim Houliston
https://amblilfeorg.files.wordpress.com/2022/04/davinciquote.jpg

2.17 – Creative Commons. Author: Crijam
https://commons.wikimedia.org/wiki/File:L%C3%A9onard_de_Vinci,
_Bille_de_verre_et_%C3%A9il_humain,_vers_1508-
09,_MS_D,_3v.jpg

2.18 – Public Domain
https://commons.wikimedia.org/wiki/File:0_The_Vitruvian_Man_-
_by_Leonardo_da_Vinci.jpg

Chapter 3: The Science of MMD

3.1 – Public Domain
https://commons.wikimedia.org/wiki/File:02_1_facies_dorsalis_cere
bri.jpg

3.2 – Creative Commons. Author: Terry Presley
https://www.flickr.com/photos/36979785@N06/6187072323/

3.3 – Photo by Jim Houliston
https://amblilfeorg.files.wordpress.com/2022/03/picsart_09-24-
09.53.47.jpg

3.4 – Public Domain
https://commons.wikimedia.org/wiki/File:US_Navy_110302-N-
9O94S-
060_Ship%27s_Serviceman_Seaman_Krista_Stelzner_draws_pictures_
with_a_child_during_a_community_service_event.jpg

2.2 – Public Domain
https:\\commons.wikimedia.org/wiki/File:%27Are_you_in_this%27_p oster.jpg

2.3 – Public Domain
https:\\www.gutenberg.org\files\15715\15715-h\images\

2.4 – Creative Commons. Author: GeorgeLouis
https:\\commons.wikimedia.org/wiki/File:Leaders_welcoming_boy_int o_Mexico_Scouting.jpg

2.5 – Public Domain
https:\\amblifeorg.files.wordpress.com\2022\04\20220412_084559.jpg

2.6 – Creative Commons. Author: Matthewpraylor
https:\\commons.wikimedia.org/wiki/File:Scouts_Aotearoa_Logo.svg

2.7 – Public Domain
https:\\commons.m.wikimedia.org/wiki/File:Robert_Baden-Powell_(von_Herkomer).jpg

2.8 – Public Domain
https:\\commons.wikimedia.org/wiki/File:BenFranklinDuplessis.jpg

2.9 – Public Domain
https:\\commons.wikimedia.org/wiki/File:HD.11.029_(10995364195).jpg

2.10 – Typesetting on display at the Benjamin Franklin Museum in Philadelphia, National Park Service. Photo taken by Jim Houliston.
https:\\amblifeorg.files.wordpress.com\2022\03\screenshot_20220120-082837_gallery.jpg

2.11 – Public Domain
https:\\commons.wikimedia.org/wiki/File:Benjamin_Franklin_1767.jpg

2.12 – "The Bond" statue of Franklin and Washington in Philadelphia by artist Jim West. Photo by Jim Houliston.
https:\\amblifeorg.files.wordpress.com\2022\03\screenshot_20220120-091855_gallery.jpg

2.13 – Public Domain
https:\\commons.wikimedia.org/wiki/File:Portrait_of_Leonardo_da_Vi nci_(from_Characatures_by_Leonardo_da_Vinci,_from_Drawings_by

Albert Einstein to become a master violinist.[28]

Figure 1.8: Thomas Jefferson taught himself to write left-handed after injuring his right wrist

Before becoming the 3rd U.S. President, the multilingual **Thomas Jefferson** was sent by Congress in 1784 to join Benjamin Franklin in France for commercial negotiations. Two years later, while still in France, Jefferson broke his right wrist. The accident forced him to begin writing with his left hand while the other rehabilitated. Jefferson continued developing dual-dominance for the remainder of his life... another 40 years![29]

The surgical pioneer and professor, **Dr. Thomas Dent Mütter**, who taught fellow surgeons years ahead of him, was considered the best in his profession. As a young surgeon in the 1830's, his ambidextrous skills astounded amphitheaters of students, surgeons, and onlookers who could not tell just which hand to follow – baffled at how they could ever replicate his otherworldly skills.[30] The doctor also collected a vast array of medical oddities, all of which can be viewed today inside his Mütter Museum in Philadelphia, Pennsylvania. This museum is also the only place in the world to have on public display slides from the brain of Albert Einstein, which will be discussed more in this chapter.[31]

American poet, Walt Whitman, described in his 1866 piece, *Left-hand writing by soldiers*, the clarity of less-dominant handwriting samples from **U.S. Civil War soldier amputees** who had quickly learned the skill out of necessity. Whitman wrote that, *"a great many* *of the specimens are written in a beautiful manner. All are good. The writing in nearly all cases slants backwards instead of forward."*[32]

The dual-dominant polymath and renaissance man, **Sir Daniel Wilson**, was knighted by Queen Victoria as a gifted artist, historian, ethnologist, poet, author, archaeologist, literary critic, and museum maker.[33] After nearly 80 years of ambidextral development, Wilson stated, *"Experience shows that wherever the early and persistent cultivation of the full use of both hands has been carried out, the result is greater efficiency, without any counterbalancing effect. We are bimanous in the best sense, and are meant to have the free, unrestrained use of both hands."*[34]

Figure 1.9: Lewis Carroll wrote various letters in mirrored direction

Alice in Wonderland author, **Lewis Carroll**, wrote over 100,000 letters to his adoring fans, and many of them were quite special.[35] Called "looking-glass letters," these were written by Carroll in mirrored script.[36] Even Carroll's illustrator, **Peter Newell**, dabbled with mirrored script when creating the earliest known, non-natural, rotational *ambigram* – a style of calligraphy with multiple spatial interpretations.[37]

Figure 1.10: Nikola Tesla described himself as ambidextrous

In his autobiography, inventor and futurist **Nikola Tesla** described himself this way – "I am ambidextrous

18

1.8 – Public Domain
https:\\commons.wikimedia.org\wiki\File:Thomas_Jefferson_by_Remb
randt_Peale,_1800.jpg

1.9 – Public Domain
https:\\commons.wikimedia.org\wiki\File:Lewis_Carroll_1863.jpg

1.10 – Public Domain
https:\\commons.wikimedia.org\wiki\File:Tesla3.jpg

1.11 – Public Domain
https:\\commons.wikimedia.org\wiki\File:GARFIELD,_James_A.-
President_(BEP_engraved_portrait).jpg

1.12 – Public Domain
https:\\commons.wikimedia.org\wiki\File:Queen_Victoria_1887_(Cro
pped).jpg

1.13 – Public Domain
https:\\commons.wikimedia.org\wiki\File:HandCuffHarryHoudini.jpg

1.14 – Public Domain
https:\\commons.wikimedia.org\wiki\File:Albert_Einstein_Head.jpg

1.15 – Public Domain
https:\\commons.wikimedia.org\wiki\File:Gandhi,_studio_picture,_19
31.jpg

1.16 – Creative Commons. Author: Pedro Ribeiro Simões
https:\\commons.wikimedia.org\wiki\File:The_Artist_-
Maurits_Cornelius_Escher-
_working_at_his_Atelier_(50385403156).jpg

1.17 – Public Domain
https:\\commons.wikimedia.org\wiki\File:Jimi-Hendrix-1967-
Helsinki.jpg

Chapter 2: The Big Three – Da Vinci, Franklin, and Baden-Powell

2.1 – Public Domain
https:\\commons.wikimedia.org\wiki\File:Baden_Powell.jpg

PICTURE CREDITS

Introduction

X.1 – Public Domain
https:\\commons.wikimedia.org/wiki/File:Ambidextric.svg

Chapter 1: History's Spectrum of MMD

1.1 – Creative Commons. Authors: Patrick J. Lynch, Medical Illustrator, and C. Carl Jaffe, MD, Cardiologist.
https:\\commons.wikimedia.org/wiki/File:Skeleton_anterior.svg

1.2 – Graphic text by Jim Houliston
https:\\amblifeorg.files.wordpress.com/2022/03/picsart_03-14-04.31.36.jpg

1.3 – Creative Commons. Author: Pearce
https:\\commons.wikimedia.org/wiki/File:Rongo_rongo_Tafel.jpg

1.4 – Public Domain
https:\\en.wikipedia.org/wiki/File:Mirror_writing2.jpg

1.5 – Creative Commons. Author: Marie-Lan Nguyen
https:\\commons.wikimedia.org/wiki/File:Plato_Silanion_Musei_Capit olini_MC1377.jpg

1.6 – Public Domain
https:\\commons.wikimedia.org/wiki/File:God2-Sistine_Chapel.png

1.7 – Public Domain
https:\\commons.wikimedia.org/wiki/File:Mozart-small.jpg

now, but then I was left-handed and had comparatively little strength in my right arm."[38]

The brilliant, yet overlooked, 20th U.S. President, **James Garfield**, mastered several languages and was the first president to campaign bilingually – in both English and German. He also developed the ability to use one hand to write Latin while, simultaneously, using the other hand to write Greek.[39]

Figure 1.11: President Garfield wrote with both hands and was multilingual

It was a tutor named **Edwin Henry Landseer** who taught England's **Queen Victoria** the use of both hands. Landseer demonstrated his talent by drawing the head of a horse with one hand and the head of a buck with the other, simultaneously.[40]

Figure 1.12: Queen Victoria was taught to use both hands by her ambidextrous tutor

Illusionist and escape artist **Harry Houdini** trained himself to become dual-dominant to better handle cards,[41] escape chains and straitjackets while hanging upside down, and generally outdo his competitor's performances.[42] Houdini even encouraged dual-dominant training for all children.[43]

In 1896, while still a professor at Princeton University, 28th U.S. President, **Woodrow Wilson**, suffered a stroke that weakened his right side. With only a little practice, Wilson started writing fluently with his left hand and continued to do so for the next year.[44]

While he was only ever photographed writing with his right hand, **Albert Einstein** had an abnormally symmetric brain. This feature produces greater connections between both brain hemispheres and typically occurs among the ambidextrous.[45] At autopsy, it was discovered that Einstein's brain had a thicker *corpus callosum*[46] and an exceptional number of *glial cells*. The corpus callosum serves as the communication bridge between our two brain hemispheres while glial cells are responsible for the speed of cognition. The more glial cells one has,

Figure 1.13: Houdini practiced dual-dominance to become a better magician

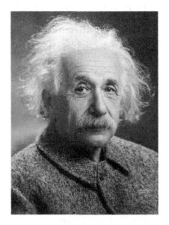

Figure 1.14: Einstein's brain shows evidence of dual-dominance

the higher their native intelligence.[47] Einstein's genius is often associated with a highly creative imagination – considered a right-brain function exercised by left-sided body movement.[48]

When talking about Einstein and his brain, it is important to clarify MMD-induced brain growth. Einstein's brain weighed 10% less than the average adult, at only 2.7 pounds.[49] If Einstein practiced a spectrum of MMD (a

9 – MirrorRead.com, "Frequently Asked Questions,"
https://www.mirrorread.com/faq

33 – Wikipedia.org, "Gordie Howe," February 1, 2022. https://wikipedia.org/wiki/Gordie_Howe

34 – Del Milligan. TheLedger.com, "Being an Ambidextrous Golfer Means Twice the Holes-in-One," March 12, 2013. https://www.theledger.com/story/news/2013/03/11/being-an-ambidextrous-golfer-means-twice-the-holes-in-one/26858952200/

Chapter 5: Mirror Reading

1 – Wikipedia.org, "Language," January 20, 2022. https://en.wikipedia.org/wiki/Language

2 – Steph Koyfman. Babbel.com, "Why Is Most Language Read From Left To Right," April 28, 2021. https://www.babbel.com/en/magazine/right-to-left-languages

3 – MirrorRead.com, "About Us," https://www.mirrorread.com/our_team

4 – MirrorRead.com, "Frequently Asked Questions," https://www.mirrorread.com/faq

5 – R.A. Poldrack, J.E. Desmond, G.H. Glover, and J.D. Gabrieli. Academic.oup.com, "The neural basis of visual skill learning: an fMRI study of mirror reading," January 1, 1998. https://academic.oup.com/cercor/article/8/1/1/339758

6 – B. Deweer, B. Pillon, A. Michon, and B. Dubois. TandFonline.com, "Mirror reading in Alzheimer's disease: Normal skill learning and acquisition of item-specific information," January 4, 2008. https://www.tandfonline.com/doi/abs/10.1080/01688639308402596

7 – Dr. Shelagh Robinson. MirrorRead.com, "Sweet Mysteries of Mirror Reading," https://www.mirrorread.com/single-post/2018/01/11/sweet-mysteries-of-mirror-reading

8 – Emma G. Ducrden and Daniele Laverdure-Dupont. JneuroSci.org, "Practice Makes Cortex," August 27, 2008. https://www.jneurosci.org/content/jneuro/28/35/8655.full.pdf

brain 'growing' activity), then shouldn't his brain be physically larger than average? Perhaps not. MMD may increase brain *efficiency* more than physical weight or mass. This would be comparable to a Ferrari weighing less than a Toyota, while still performing much faster.

The Indian civil rights activist, **Mahatma Gandhi**, was a dominant right-hander who developed the ability to write lefty to become not solely dependent on his right hand.[50]

The visual master of otherworldly graphic design, **M.C. Escher**, developed dual-dominance at a young age.[51] He was forced to write and draw right-handed in school. Escher wrote, *"I was exclusively left-handed from my earliest childhood. At primary school I found learning to write with*

Figure 1.15: Gandhi could write with both hands

my right hand extremely difficult. I would probably have managed to write in mirror image with my left hand far more easily and naturally."

Figure 1.16: M.C. Escher preferred using his left hand, but was forced to use his right hand in school

Escher followed in the footsteps of his teacher, **Samuel Jessurun de Mesquita**, who also developed dual-dominance. As a graphic artist dealing with both traditional- and mirrored-image, Escher's ambidexterity proved highly valuable for creating stunning works of spatially mesmerizing art.In 1953, Escher produced a left-handedness survey for draftsmen and graphic artists. In the survey, Escher asked questions related to dual-dominance and advanced spatial awareness. Questions included, *"Aside from with the left hand, can you also draw, engrave and cut with the right one effortlessly (e.g. a human profile rotated to the left with the right hand just as easily as a profile rotated to the right with the left)?"*

Electric guitar legend, **Jimi Hendrix**, preferred different hands for different tasks. His left hand was used to play his right-handed guitar upside down, throw, comb his hair, and hold cigarettes.[52] His right was used for writing, eating, and talking on the phone. Hendrix's father believed that left-handed guitar playing was a sign of the devil. To prevent having his guitar taken away, Hendrix learned to play right-handed whenever his dad was present.[53]

Figure 1.17: Jimi Hendrix played guitar lefty but was forced to play righty by his dad. He also performed various tasks using alternate hands

24 – Sandra Levy. HealthLine.com, "Walking May Boost Your Creativity," October 20, 2018. healthline.com/health-news/walking-indoors-outdoors-increases-creativity-042814

25 – Ekua Hagan. PsychologyToday.com, "Einstein's Genius Linked to Well-Connected Brain Hemispheres," October 5, 2013. https://www.psychologytoday.com/us/blog/the-athletes-way/201310/einsteins-genius-linked-well-connected-brain-hemispheres

26 – Diego Irigoyen. Lettering-Daily.com, "How to Become Ambidextrous in 6 Easy Steps," https://www.lettering-daily.com/6-steps-to-become-ambidextrous/

27 – Dr. Thomas Ball. PerformanceHealthCenter.com, "Use Your Left Hand to Be in Your Right Mind," February 28, 2019. https://performancehealthcenter.com/2019/02/use-your-left-hand-to-be-in-your-right-mind/

28 – AnatomyTrains.com, "A Brief History of Anatomy Trains," https://www.anatomytrains.com/about-us/history/

29 – Giovanni Roselli. WckMethod.com, "Non-Dominant Side Training Tips to Elevate Your Performance," April 8, 2016. https://www.wckmethod.com/articles/non-dominant-side-training-tips-to-elevate-your-performance

30 – Beverly Hosford. AceFitness.org, "10 Daily Habits That Can Cause Muscular Imbalances," December 4, 2015. https://www.acefitness.org/education-and-resources/professional/expert-articles/5760/10-daily-habits-that-can-cause-muscular-imbalances/

31 – John Murphy. MDLinx.com, "5 sports scientifically proven to help you live longer," April 20, 2020. https://www.mdlinx.com/article/5-sports-scientifically-proven-to-help-you-live-longer/UbY9y7i7J204tB63p3pEy0zB

32 – Andrew Treddinick. DailyOrange.com, "TENNIS: Orange confuses opponents with ambidextrous serving," February 8, 2011. dailyorange.com/2011/02/tennis-orange-confuses-opponents-with-ambidextrous-serving/

12 – Michael J. Lavery, Whole Brain Power: The Fountain of Youth for your Mind (Lulu Press, 2008), page xiv

13 – Jim Houliston. YouTube.com, "WBM – Ultra Ball Walking" https://www.youtube.com/channel/UC2K8_AlexIDEAQ1Piz1OLJW channel.

14 – Michael J. Lavery, Whole Brain Power: The Fountain of Youth for your Mind (Lulu Press, 2008), page 153

15 – Michael J. Lavery, YouTube.com, "Ambidextrous Pitcher Church Wellick," June 23, 2008.
https://www.youtube.com/watch?v=xTzDJEPH9IM

16 – Michael J. Lavery, Whole Brain Power: The Fountain of Youth for your Mind (Lulu Press, 2008), page 213

17 – Ibid., page 210

18 – Diego Trujolyn. Lettering-Daily.com, "How to Become Ambidextrous in 6 Easy Steps," https://www.lettering-daily.com/6-steps-to-become-ambidextrous/

19 – Diego Trujolyn. Creative Brain Training: Increase Attention Span, Build Confidence, and Stimulate Creativity (Independently published, 2018), page 7

20 – Courtney E. Ackerman, M.A. PositivePsychology.com, "What is Neuroplasticity? A Psychologist Explains," May 2, 2022. https://positivepsychology.com/neuroplasticity/

21 – Jim Houliston. YouTube.com, "Extended Interview with Epiya Jeremy, Captain of Team USA Beach Handball," September 21, 2021. https://www.youtube.com/watch?v=Cldw-KJO4C8

22 – Jim Houliston. YouTube.com, "My WMD Lifestyle – Jim Houliston," January 12, 2022. https://www.youtube.com/watch?v=mF_1HiNDIA&t=1059s

23 – Jim Houliston. YouTube.com, "Interview with Dr. Kathryn Ko, Ambidextrous Neurosurgeon and Fine Artist," September 12, 2021. https://www.youtube.com/watch?v=OR_1PEj9JT&t=56s

CHAPTER 2

The Big Three: Da Vinci, Franklin, and Baden-Powell

While the previous MMD practitioners showcased exceptional skill throughout their lives, three historic individuals (aka the Big 3) provide us with additional details into their relationship with MMD – Lord Robert Baden-Powell, Benjamin Franklin, and Leonardo da Vinci.

- **Lord Robert Baden-Powell,** the 19th-century British General, royal spy, founder of the Boy Scouts, and real-life *Indiana Jones* wrote, *"To train the human body completely and symmetrically…is an obligation that cannot safely be ignored."*
- **Benjamin Franklin** was courted by kings as one of the most interesting men of the 18th century. His accomplishments in science, literature, diplomacy, business, and civic development remain influential to this day. Franklin wrote of the need to *equally educate and develop both hands.*
- **Leonardo da Vinci** mastered architecture, engineering, mechanics, and painting as the greatest creative of the Italian Renaissance. Da Vinci *wrote with both hands in various directions,* including traditional, mirrored, and inverted.

https://performancehealthcenter.com/2019/02/use-your-left-hand-to-be-in-your-right-mind/

2 – Beat-Fitness.com, "Non-Dominant Side Training," https://www.beat-fitness.com/non-dominant-side-training/

3 – Michael J. Lavery. Whole Brain Power: The Fountain of Youth for the Mind and Body (Lulu Press, 2008), page 136

4 – Diego Irigoyen. Creative Brain Training: Increase Attention Span, Build Confidence, and Stimulate Creativity (Independently published, 2018), page 20

5 – Bob Yirka. Phys.org, "Left and right brain hemispheres found to store memory differently in ants," May 6, 2020. https://phys.org/news/2020-05-left-brain-hemispheres-memories-differently.html

6 – David Wolman. A Left-Hand Turn Around the World: Chasing the Mystery and Meaning of All Things Southpaw (De Capo Press, 2005), page 129

7 – Anthony Metivier. MagneticMemoryMethod.com, "Ambidextrousness and Memory: Can Dual Handedness Boost Your Brain?" April 7, 2021. https://www.magneticmemorymethod.com/ambidextrousness/

8 – John Jackson. Ambidexterity; Or Two-Handedness and Two-Brainedness, An Argument For Natural Development And Rational Education. (Dryden House London, 1905), page 133

9 – Michael J. Lavery. Whole Brain Power: The Fountain of Youth for the Mind and Body (Lulu Press, 2008), page 21

10 – PsychologyAnswers.com, "What is the meaning of spatial reasoning?," https://psichologyanswers.com/library/lecture/read/554926-what-is-the-meaning-of-spatial-reasoning

11 – Steve Steinberg. WebMD.com, "Strengthen the Nondominant Side of Your Body," https://www.webmd.com/fitness-exercise/features/strengthen-the-nondominant-side-of-your-body#1

41 – Olivia Guy-Evans, SimplyPsychology.org, "Broca's Area Function and Location," June 28, 2021. https:\\www.simplypsychology.org\broca-area.html

42 – Jason G. Goldman, BBC.com, "Evolution: Why are most of us right-handed?" December 15, 2014. https:\\www.bbc.com\future\article\20141215-why-are-most-of-us-right-handed

43 – Michael J. Lavery, Whole Brain Power: The Fountain of Youth for the Mind and Body (Lulu Press, 2008), page 101

44 – Chris McManus, Right Hand, Left Hand: The Origins of Asymmetry in Brains, Bodies, Atoms and Cultures (Orion Publishing, 2003), page 348

45 – Katja Guenther, NCBI.NLM.NIH.gov, "'It's All Done With Mirrors': V.S. Ramachandran and the Material Culture of Phantom Limb Research," July 2016. https:\\www.ncbi.nlm.nih.gov\pmc\articles\PMC4904333\

46 – Rachael Lowe, Physio-pedia.com, "Mirror Therapy," February 3, 2022. https:\\www.physio-pedia.com\Mirror_Therapy

47 – Thomas Politzer, O.D. BrainLine.org, "Vision Is Our Dominant Sense," July 26, 2018. https:\\www.brainline.org\article\vision-our-dominant-sense

48 – Patrick Cohn, PeakSports.com, "Sports Visualization: The Secret Weapon of Athletes," https:\\www.peaksports.com\sports-psychology-blog\sports-visualization-athletes\

49 – Anastasia Harazdabidou, Virgin.com, "Great ideas: Is imagination more important than knowledge," February 12, 2015. https:\\www.virgin.com\about-virgin\latest\great-ideas-imagination-more-important-knowledge

Chapter 4: The Benefits of MMD

1 – Dr. Thomas Ball, PerformanceHealthCenter.com, "Use Your Left Hand to Be in Your Right Mind," Februart 28, 2019.

Lord Robert Baden-Powell

Figure 2.1: Baden-Powell becomes a national hero after defending the town of Mafeking in South Africa

Baden-Powell shared his many skills with the youth – teaching them self-discipline, leadership, and education on the wonders of our natural world. Baden-Powell's past includes serving as a British General, Crown spy, author, artist, musician, and Founder of the international Scouting movement. Born in 1857, Baden-Powell's love of nature often led him to sneak out of school and spend time in the woods. There, he would observe nature, hunt for food, hike, canoe, and hone survival skills. These later became a key focus of the Boy Scouts.[1]

Figure 2.2: World War I poster art created by Baden-Powell

24

In 1899, Baden-Powell commanded a garrison of 217 troops to defend a town from 8,000 Boer army soldiers during the Siege of Mafeking in South Africa.[2] This made him a hero back in England, and earned him a promotion to Major-General by Queen Victoria.[3] He also had a three-year post as a spy on the Island of Malta. There, he disguised himself as an entomologist and hid secret details of enemy fortifications and elevation contours within his drawings of leaves, moths, and butterflies.[4]

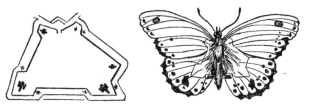

Figure 2.3: As a spy, Baden-Powell concealed details of enemy fortresses inside his nature drawings, like at the center of this symmetric butterfly (secret details of corner guns and cannons expanded at right)

Baden-Powell descriptively wove his many skills together in writing. His most famous book, *Scouting for Boys*, was used by British teachers and community leaders to instruct youth. It became the fourth best-selling book of the 20th century and, inadvertently, started the international movement known as the Boy Scouts.[5]

By the end of 1910, a mere three years after holding his first camp of just 22 boys on Brownsea Island, there were over 100,000 Scouts in England. Baden-Powell retired from the Army to focus exclusively on promoting Scouting. By 1922, there were more than a million scouts in 32 countries. By 1939, the number of Scouts had grown to over 3 million.

23 – Ibid., page 138

24 – Ibid., page 55

25 – Ibid., page 61

26 – Ibid., page 147

27 – Ibid., page 143

28 – David Wolman. A Left-Hand Turn Around the World: Chasing the Mystery and Meaning of All Things Lefty (De Capo Press, 2005), page 120

29 – Ibid., page 121

30 – Ibid., page 194

31 – Michael J. Gelb. Whole Brain Power: The Fountain of Youth for the Mind and Body (Lulu Press, 2008), page 21

32 – Robert H. Shmerling, MD. Harvard Health. "Right brain/left brain right," November 8, 2019. https://www.health.harvard.edu/blog/right-brain-left-brain-right-201710812525217080102

33 – David Wolman. A Left-Hand Turn Around the World: Chasing the Mystery and Meaning of All Things Lefty (De Capo Press, 2005), pages 126 & 135

34 – Ibid., page 64

35 – Michael J. Gelb. Whole Brain Power: The Fountain of Youth for the Mind and Body (Lulu Press, 2008), page 141

36 – Ibid., page 155

37 – Ibid., page 152

38 – Diego Trujovich. Creating Brain Traction: Increase Attention Span, Build Confidence, and Stimulate Creativity (Independently published, 2018), page 21

39 – Michael J. Gelb. Whole Brain Power: The Fountain of Youth for the Mind and Body (Lulu Press, 2008), page 153

40 – Ibid., page 154

11 – "Grand Wanderer." Instructables.com, "How to Develop Ambidexterity," 2013. https://www.instructables.com/How-to-Develop-Ambidexterity/

12 – Andreas Roller. BlurbSlate.com, "Are the pedals the same in a left hand drive car?" March 3, 2021. https://blurbslate.com/are-the-pedals-the-same-in-a-left-hand-drive-car

13 – Michael J. Lavery. Whole Brain Power: The Fountain of Youth for the Mind and Body (Lulu Press, 2008), page 50

14 – Allison Wild. BuzzFeed.com, "17 Everyday Objects That Are Useless To Left-Handed People," July 18, 2017. https://www.buzzfeed.com/allisonwild/its-a-righty-word-were-just-living-in-it

15 – Tracey le Roux. OT-Mom-Learning-Activities.com, "Is Your Child Switching Hands?" https://www.ot-mom-learning-activities.com/switching-hands.html

16 – Michael J. Lavery. Whole Brain Power: The Fountain of Youth for the Mind and Body (Lulu Press, 2008), page 204

17 – Chris McManus. Right Hand, Left Hand: The Origins of Asymmetry in Brains, Bodies, Atoms and Cultures (Orion Publishing, 2003), page 179

18 – Multiple Contributors. Reviewed by Dan Brennan, MD. WebMD.com, "The Difference Between the Left and Right Brain," April 15, 2021. https://www.webmd.com/brain/the-difference-between-the-left-and-right-brain

19 – Michael J. Lavery. Whole Brain Power: The Fountain of Youth for the Mind and Body (Lulu Press, 2008), page xii

20 – Chris McManus. Right Hand, Left Hand: The Origins of Asymmetry in Brains, Bodies, Atoms and Cultures (Orion Publishing, 2003), page 242

21 – Ibid., page 238

22 – Michael J. Lavery. Whole Brain Power: The Fountain of Youth for the Mind and Body (Lulu Press, 2008), page 54

Figure 2.4: The official Scout Handshake is left-handed to develop dual-dominance

Baden-Powell was a practitioner and strong promoter of MMD.[6] A few years before starting the Boy Scouts, he served as Vice President of the *Ambidextral Culture Society* and wrote the introduction to their book – *Ambidexterity: Or Two-Handedness and Two-Brainedness, An Argument For Natural Development And Rational Education.* Written in 1905 by the organization's Secretary, John Jackson – a Scottish school teacher – *Ambidexterity* presents the science, history, and perceptions of dual-dominance as a beneficial practice to all.[7]

Within the book's Introduction, Baden-Powell tells us,

"**I have long been accustomed to write with either hand** or to use the two hands interchangeably. To **train** the human body completely and **symmetrically**, that is, to cultivate all its organs and members to their utmost capacity, in order that its functions may also attain their **maximum development**, is an obligation that cannot safely be ignored. This **completeness** and symmetry can only be secured by an equal attention to, and exercise of, both sides of the body – the right and the left; and this **two-sided growth can alone be promoted and matured by educating our two hands equally**, each in precisely the same way, and exactly to the same extent.

"Our hands – and our arms, from which, for purposes both of argument and education, they cannot be separated – not only constitute our chief medium of communication with the outer world, but they are likewise the preeminent agency by which we stamp our impress upon it. Moreover, and of equal import to the individual, it is by the movements of these members that the whole muscular tissues on both sides of the body are exercised, strengthened, and perfected.

"There is no doubt that the value of ambidexterity from a military point of view is immense. I do not consider a man is a thoroughly trained soldier unless he can mount equally well on either side of his horse, use the sword, pistol, and lance, equally well with both hands, and shoot off the left shoulder as rapidly and accurately as from the right.

"I wish I had cultivated in my youth the useful art of writing on two different subjects at once. I get through a great deal extra by using the right and left hand alternately, but I thoroughly appreciate how much more can be done by using them both together."

This Introduction ends with Baden-Powell signing his name, both, left- and right-handed.

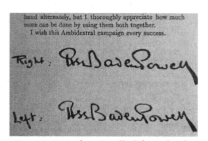

Figure 2.5: Baden-Powell's left- and right-handed signatures

Baden-Powell is no exception to a polymathic tendency ambidexters have to excel in various fields,[8] as reflected in the introduction of *merit badges* – 57 of which were introduced to the Boy Scouts of America in its infancy.[9] These badges covered a vast spectrum of disciplines, ranging from Archery to Astronomy, Aviation to Business, Chemistry to Painting, Public Health to Sculpture, and many more. One can also argue that Baden-Powell's aptitude for knot tying, observation, and orienteering came from a

https://qbi.uq.edu.au/article/2019/02/why-our-brain-most-intelligent-machine-all

2 – Tanya Lewis and Ashley P. Taylor. LiveScience.com, "Human brain: Facts, function & anatomy," May 28, 2021. https://www.livescience.com/29365-human-brain.html

3 – Todd Townes. ShareCare.com, "How many calories does the brain consume," https://www.sharecare.com/health/calories/brain-calories-at-rest

4 – Meghan Jones. RD.com, "10 Fascinating Facts You Never Knew About Ambidextrous People," May 29, 2019. https://www.rd.com/list/facts-ambidextrous-people/

5 – David Wolman. A Left-Hand Turn Around the World: Chasing the Mystery and Meaning of All Things Southpaw (De Capo Press, 2005), page 48

6 – Vivian Lam. ScopeBlog.Stanford.edu, " "We know very little about the brain:" Experts outline challenges in neuroscience," November 8, 2016, https://scopeblog.stanford.edu/2016/11/08/challenges-in-neuroscience-in-the-21st-century/

7 – Eero Vuoksimaa. NCBI.NLM.NIH.gov, "Origins of Handedness: A nationwide study of 30161 adults," January 16, 2009. https://www.ncbi.nlm.nih.gov/pmc/articles/PMC2680751/

8 – Olivia Guy-Evans. SimplyPsychology.org, "Lateralization of Brain Function," May 18, 2021. https://www.simplypsychology.org/brain-lateralization.html

9 – Michael Corballis. ScientificAmerican.com, "Can Training to Become Ambidextrous Improve Brain Function," March 1, 2013. https://www.scientificamerican.com/article/can-training-to-become-ambidextrous-improve-brain-function/

10 – Kendra Cherry. VeryWellMind.com, "Left Brain Vs. Right Brain Dominance," April 10, 2020. https://www.verywellmind.com/left-brain-vs-right-brain-2795005

55 – Leonardo da Vinci, translated by Jean Paul Richter (1888). The Complete Notebooks of Leonardo da Vinci (Eternal Sun Books, 2016), page 9

56 – History.com, "Leonardo da Vinci," December 2, 2009. https://www.history.com/topics/renaissance/leonardo-da-vinci

57 – Diego Irigoyen. Creative Brain Training: Increase Attention Span, Build Confidence, and Stimulate Creativity (Independently published, 2018), page 30

58 – 'Haunty.', Owlcation.com, "Leonardo da Vinci's Camera Obscura," December 22, 2016. https://owlcation.com/humanities/Leonardo-da-Vincis-Camera-Obscura

59 – Melissa Kelly. ThoughtCo.com, "Spatial Intelligence," May 30, 2019. https://www.thoughtco.com/spatial-intelligence-profile-8096

60 – Leonardo da Vinci, translated by Jean Paul Richter (1888). The Complete Notebooks of Leonardo da Vinci (Eternal Sun Books, 2016), page 26

61 – Diego Irigoyen. Creative Brain Training: Increase Attention Span, Build Confidence, and Stimulate Creativity (Independently published, 2018), page 43

62 – Darren Rousar. SightSize.com, "The Mirror – The Master of Painters," September 2021. https://www.sightsize.com/the-mirror-the-master-of-painters/

63 – Rachel Suhs. Coere.co, "Think Like a Genius: What Would Leonardo da Vinci Do with Today's" https://coere.co/davinci-reflections/

64 – Pooja Shah. Procaffenation.com, "Codex Leicester; The World's Most Expensive Book," July 10, 2020. https://procaffenation.com/codex-leicester/

Chapter 3: The Science of MMD

1 – Queensland Brain Institute. QBI.edu.au, "Why our brain is the most intelligent machine of all," February 1, 2019.

heightened spatial awareness that was brought on by his own practice of MMD.[10] Even the very first knot a scout is required to learn – the square knot – is simple, symmetric, and tied using mirrored movement.[11] It is seen on the Scouting International logo, which features a symmetric fleur-de-lis – a shape that is drawn, ideally, using both hands.

Figure 2.6: Scouting International logo: Symmetric, featuring the MMD-tied square knot

Baden-Powell's enthusiasm for MMD, and desire to see it practiced by others, is demonstrated by his choice to make the official handshake of the Boy Scouts a simple, left-handed handshake.[12] In 1931, the Governor of Queensland, Lieutenant General Sir John Goodwin, recalled how Baden-

Powell, "*stressed the desirability of ambidextral training among the Scouts, his contention being that Nature never meant that the left hand should be idle while the right one is working. In the same way it is customary among Scouts to use the left when shaking hands.*" Goodwin also commented that Baden-Powell could draw equally well with both hands.[13]

Figure 2.7: Baden-Powell writing left-handed

When Baden-Powell, a man so dedicated to the equal under-standing and balance of both sides of his body, died in 1941, he was buried near the center of where Earth's northern and southern hemispheres meet, a short distance from the Equator, in Nyeri, Kenya.

Benjamin Franklin

One multilingual polymath who lived when using the left hand was considered unacceptable – even 'sinister' – was Benjamin Franklin. Franklin became a household name through his various areas of expertise. He was a printer, publisher, businessman, diplomat, inventor, scientist, philosopher, U.S. Founding Father, and a writer.[14] His autobiography, although incomplete, became one of the most famous and influential of all time, recounting many of his life's personal

Figure 2.8: Franklin is one of history's foremost polymaths

details.[15] Within this work, though, Franklin never mentioned his own handedness, even though various sources consider him dual-dominant.[16]

It was while writing his autobiography that Franklin penned a separate essay called, *A Petition of the Left Hand.*[17] Like many of his essays, Franklin adopts a pseudonym, this one being a feminine characterization of the Left Hand. Written in 1779, Franklin's *Petition* creatively implores educators to stop forcing exclusive right-handedness – and instead, instruct the development of both hands.

29

45 – AirAndSpace.si.edu, "Leonardo da Vinci's Codex on the Flight of Birds," October 22, 2013. https://airandspace.si.edu/exhibitions/codex/

46 – Da-Vinci-Inventions.com, "Leonardo Da Vinci Inventions," 2019. https://www.da-vinci-inventions.com/flying-machine

47 – Wikipedia.org, "Aristotle," March 29, 2022. https://en.wikipedia.org/wiki/Aristotle

48 – PalmariumArchive.com, "Aristotle and Socrates on Beauty," July 12, 2013. https://palmariumarchive.wordpress.com/2013/07/12/aristotle-and-socrates-on-beauty-im/

49 – Janice Bell, Academia.edu, "Aristotle as a Source for Leonardo's Theory of Colour Perspective after 1500," Journal of the Warburg and Courtauld Institutes, Vol 56, (1993) pp. 100-118. The Warburg Institute. https://www.academia.edu/7526075/Aristotle_as_a_Source_for _Leonardos_Theory_of_Colour_Perspective_after_1500

50 – Jefferson.edu, "Was Leonardo Da Vinci's Dyslexia Responsible for His Brilliance?," May 7, 2019. https://www.jefferson.edu/university/news/2019/05/7/dyslexia-helped- leonardo-davinci.html

51 – Brigit Katz, SmithsonianMag.com, "Was Leonardo da Vinci, a Famous Lefty, Actually Ambidextrous?," April 11, 2019. https://www.smithsonianmag.com/smart-news/was-leonardo-da-vinci-famous-lefty-actually-ambidextrous-180971938/

52 – Michael J. Lavery. Whole Brain Power: The Fountain of Youth for the Mind and Body (Lulu Press, 2008), page 138

53 – Diego Irigoyen. Creative Brain Training: Increase Attention Span, Build Confidence, and Stimulate Creativity (Independently published, 2018), page 28

54 – Michael J. Lavery. Whole Brain Power: The Fountain of Youth for the Mind and Body (Lulu Press, 2008), page 152

https:\\www.cnbc.com\2019\03\08\when-and-why-daylight-saving-time-started-in-the-us.html

37 – 'Bobby', UPSBatteryCenter.com, "Contribution of Benjamin Franklin to Electricity," June 6, 2014. https:\\www.upsbatterycenter.com\blog\contribution-benjamin-franklin-electricity\

LEONARDO DA VINCI

37 – Wikipedia.org, "Leonardo da Vinci," January 23, 2022. https:\\wikipedia.org\wiki\Leonardo_da_Vinci

38 – Warehouse-13-Artifact-Database-Wiki.com, "Leonardo da Vinci's Notebook," https:\\warehouse-13-artifact-database.fandom.com\wiki\Leonardo_da_Vinci%27s_Notebook

39 – Mindy Weisberger, LiveScience.com, "Leonardo Da Vinci Was Ambidextrous, Handwriting Analysis Shows," April 15, 2019. https:\\www.livescience.com\65225-da-vinci-ambidextrous.html

40 – Chris McManus, Right Hand, Left Hand: The Origins of Asymmetry in Brains, Bodies, Atoms and Cultures (Orion Publishing, 2003), pages 349–350

41 – Michael J. Lavery. Whole Brain Power: The Fountain of Youth for the Mind and Body (Lulu Press, 2008), page 137

42 – Memento Artem. ClockTower. Ucollege.edu, "Leonardo da Vinci: Corpse Caper," September 19, 2018. https:\\clocktower.ucollege.edu\articles\2018\leonardo-da-vinci-corpse-caper

43 – Ludwig Heinrich Heydenreich. Britannica.com, "Anatomical studies and drawings of Leonardo da Vinci," https:\\www.britannica.com\biography\Leonardo-da-Vinci\Anatomical-studies-and-drawings

44 – Jackie Craven. ThoughtCo.com, "Symmetry and Proportion in Design: What Leonardo Da Vinci Learned From Vitruvius," July 17, 2018. https:\\www.thoughtco.com\symmetry-and-proportion-in-design-177569

Franklin excelled in many areas throughout his life, but what qualified him to make such an assertion to educators? Quite a bit, actually. Considered to be America's first millionaire,[18] Franklin once said, in reference to education, "If a man empties his purse into his head, no man can take it away from him. An investment in knowledge always pays the best interest."[19]

Figure 2.9: After retiring at 42, Franklin spent much of his time scientifically studying electricity, subsequently inventing the Lightning Rod. This made him an international celebrity

Even more, Franklin started what became America's first university after writing an essay in 1749 titled, *Proposals Relating to the Education of Youth.*[20] Using this essay, he organized 24 trustees to form an institution of higher education that challenged conventions of the day. Thirty years later, in 1779, this institution became the University of Pennsylvania. It was during this same year that Franklin wrote *A Petition of the Left Hand.* As if writing to his own, new university, Franklin addressed the essay "to those who have the **Superintendency of Education.**"

Details from the essay mention the feminine left hand being beaten for attempting to make herself useful. From what sounds like the personification of an unforgettably unpleasant left-handed childhood, the 73-year-old Franklin had years to reflect on such a struggle. In doing so, he lists good justification for the equal use and development of both hands – a hallmark of any proud ambidexter.

Would this fascinating man practice MMD if alive today? A close look at his *Petition* suggests that, yes, he would. Read the essay for yourself and see if you agree.

"A Petition of the Left Hand"

by Benjamin Franklin

To Those Who Have the **Superintendency of Education,**

I address myself to all the friends of youth and conjure them to direct their compassionate regards to my unhappy fate, in order to remove the prejudices of which I am the victim. There are twin sisters of us; and the two eyes of man do not more resemble, nor are capable of being upon better terms with each other, than my sister and myself, were it not for the partiality of our parents, who make **the most injurious distinctions between us.** *From my infancy, I have been led to consider my sister as a being of a more elevated rank. I was suffered to grow up without the least instruction, while nothing was spared in her education. She had masters to teach her writing, drawing, music, and other accomplishments; but if by chance I touched a pencil, a pen, or a needle, I was bitterly rebuked; and more than once I have been beaten for being awkward and wanting a graceful manner. It is true, my sister associated me with her upon some occasions; but she always made a point of taking the lead, calling upon me only from necessity, or to figure by her side.*

But conceive not, sirs, that my complaints are instigated merely by vanity. No; my uneasiness is occasioned by an object much more serious. It is the practice in our family, that the whole business of providing for its

31

25 – Benjamin-Franklin-History.org, "Benjamin Franklin, the Printer," http://www.benjamin-franklin-history.org/benjamin-franklin-printer/

26 – SlaveryAndRemembrance.org, "Printer and Binder," https://www.slaveryandremembrance.org/Almanack/life/trades/tradepri. cfm?showSite=mobile-regular

27 – PBS, YouTube.com, "Benjamin Franklin Makes a Name for Himself as a Printer | PBS | Ken Burns," April 4, 2022. https://www.youtube.com/watch?v=mAN9zW31Jdg

28 – NPS.gov, "Benjamin Franklin's Resume," https://www.nps.gov/inde/learn/historyculture/people-franklin-resume.htm

29 – Chris McManus, Right Hand, Left Hand: The Origins of Asymmetry in Brains, Bodies, Atoms and Cultures (Orion Publishing, 2003), page 348

30 – Benjamin-Franklin-History.org, "Timeline," http://www.benjamin-franklin-history.org/timeline/

31 – Charlie Rose, YouTube.com, "Walter Isaacson interview on Benjamin Franklin (2003)," February 10, 2017. https://www.youtube.com/watch?v=LMhOjS1LSSw

32 – Meka Books, YouTube.com, "The Autobiography of Benjamin Franklin [Summary & Outline]," July 25, 2021. https://www.youtube.com/watch?v=7TLhT9MFFA4

33 – CliffNotes.com, "About The Autobiography of Benjamin Franklin," http://cliffsnotes.com/literature/a/the-autobiography-of-benjamin-franklin/about-the-autobiography-of-benjamin-franklin

34 – Evan Andrews, History.com, "11 Surprising Facts About Benjamin Franklin," August 19, 2020. https://www.history.com/news/11-surprising-facts-about-benjamin-franklin

35 – Independence Hall Association, USHistory.org, "Swim Fins," https://www.ushistory.org/franklin/science/swimfins.htm

36 – Kathleen Elkins, CNBC.com, "Here's when and why daylight saving time started in the US," March 6, 2020.

14 – Wikipedia.org, "Benjamin Franklin," February 21, 2022. https://wikipedia.org/wiki/Benjamin_Franklin

15 – Wikipedia.org, "The Autobiography of Benjamin Franklin," January 31, 2022. https://wikipedia.org/wiki/The_Autobiography_of_Benjamin_Franklin

16 – MSN.com, "Athletes and A-listers who are ambidextrous," December 10, 2021. https://www.msn.com/en-us/travel/news/athletes-and-a-listers-who-are-ambidextrous/ss-AARET0t#image=10

17 – Benjamin Franklin. LeftHandersLegacy.org, "A Petition of the Left Hand," 1779. https://lefthanderslegacy.org/left-handed-profiles/a-petition-of-the-left-hand-by-benjamin-franklin/

18 – J.V. Crum III. ConsciousMillionaire.com, "Become the 1ˢᵗ Millionaire in Your Family," 2014. https://consciousmillionaire.com/PDF/1ST-MILLIONAIRE.pdf

19 – Barry Popik. BarryPopik.com, "An investment in knowledge always pays the best interest," November 4, 2014. https://www.barrypopik.com/index.php/new_york_city/entry/an_investment_in_knowledge

20 – Upenn.edu, "Penn's History," https://www.upenn.edu/about/history

21 – J.L. Bell. Boston1775.blogspot.com, "Benjamin Franklin: Lefty or Righty?," May 7, 2009. https://boston1775.blogspot.com/2009/05/benjamin-franklin-lefty-or-righty.html

22 – LeftHandersLegacy.org, "Benjamin Franklin," 2018. https://lefthanderslegacy.org/benjamin-franklin/

23 – Melvin D. Saunders. Mind-Course.com, "Let Us Introduce You To Our New Ambidexterity Exercise," 2013. http://www.mind-course.com/ambi.html

24 – Chris McManus. Right Hand, Left Hand: The Origins of Asymmetry in Brains, Bodies, Atoms and Cultures (Orion Publishing, 2003), page 330

*subsistence falls upon my sister and myself. If any indisposition should attack my sister—and I mention it in confidence upon this occasion, that she is subject to the gout, the rheumatism, and cramp, without making mention of other accidents—what would be the fate of our poor family? Must not the regret of our parents be excessive, at having placed so great a difference between **sisters who are so perfectly equal**? Alas! we must perish from distress; for it would not be in my power even to scrawl a suppliant petition for relief, having been obliged to employ the hand of another in transcribing the request which I have now the honor to prefer to you.*

*Condescend, sirs, to make my parents sensible of **the injustice of an exclusive tenderness**, and of **the necessity of distributing their care and affection among all their children equally**.*

I am, with a profound respect, Sirs, your most obedient servant,

The Left Hand

The essay's main themes:

- Addressed to educators the same year Franklin's school becomes America's first university
- Classified both left and right hands as natural equals in need of equal development
- Listed detrimental/wasteful results from forcing a child to use primarily one hand
- Cited using both hands as necessary to survival in case of accident

So, was Franklin right-handed, left-handed, mix-handed, or dual-dominant? This essay, written in the voice of the abused and underdeveloped left hand, laments a general, cultural neglect of the southpaw side; an odd grievance to be made by any exclusive right-hander. And, while a 1762 painting shows Franklin holding a quill in his right hand,[21] some sources say he was left-handed,[22] including that he signed both the Declaration of Independence and the U.S. Constitution left-handed.[23] He is also portrayed in the movie *1776* as a lefty. So, was he dual-dominant? Professor of Medical Education and Psychology, Chris McManus, a handedness expert and author of *Right Hand, Left Hand: the Origins of Asymmetry in Brains, Bodies, Atoms, and Cultures,* says the *Petition* essay suggests Franklin either held a belief in dual-dominance or was just playing a literary joke.[24]

Figure 2.10: "Fish and Visitors stink after three days." Since the age of 12, Franklin set and read mirrored print type just like this.

There is another sign, though, that Franklin practiced MMD. He was a printing apprentice to his oldest brother, James, who started the second newspaper in America, *The New-England Courant.* Since the age of 12, Franklin's job was to prepare the printing by setting type.[25] All of these metallic type settings were mirror-imaged so as to be viewed in the traditional direction once printed on paper![26]

https://www.atlasobscura.com/articles/the-founder-of-the-boy-scouts-
did-in-recent-dramwip

5 — Wikipedia.org, "Scouting for Boys", January 2, 2022.
https://wikipedia.org/wiki/Scouting_for_Boys

6 — Jim Hornfister, YourTube.com, "The Ambidexterity of Lord Robert
Baden-Powell — Boy Scouts' Founders", September 21, 2021.
https://www.youtube.com/watch?v=eJUHTZUXAQI

7 — Prerna Chawla, Medium.com, "Should Students be Trained to be
Ambidextrous", August 6, 2020. https://medium.com/indian-
thoughts/should-students-be-trained-to-be-ambidextrous-
6056c04b25d

8 — Wikipedia.org, "Polymath", January 28, 2022.
https://wikipedia.org/wiki/Polymath

9 — Steve Henning, Scouter.us, "Merit Badges, Past and Present, And
Their Evolution", February 14, 2018.
https://www.scouter.us/merit-byp

10 — Michael J. Lavery, Whole Brain Power: The Fountain of Youth for
the Mind and Body (Lulu Press, 2008), page 143

11 — Melanie Radzicki McMahon, HowStuffWorks.com, "How to Tie
the Impossible Knot", June 18, 2015.
https://adventure.howstuffworks.com/survival/wilderness/how-
to-tie-the-impossible-knot.htm

12 — Charlie Wood, BrainFacts.org, "Does Using Your Non-Dominant
Hand Make You Smarter", August 6, 2019.
https://www.brainfacts.org/sitecore/content/Home/Brain-Facts2/Thinking-
sensing-and-Behaving/Thinking-and-Awareness/2019/Does-Using-
You-Non-Dominant-Hand-Make-You-Smarter-080619

13 — The Brisbane Courier, Trove.nla.gov.au, "Lord Baden-Powell's
Ambidexterity", June 2, 1931.
https://trove.nla.gov.au/newspaper/article/21716043

BENJAMIN FRANKLIN

48 – David Wolman. *A Left-Hand Turn Around the World: Chasing the Mystery and Meaning of All Things Southpaw* (De Capo Press, 2005), page 202.

49 – Wikipedia.org, "Albert Einstein's brain," February 17, 2022. https://wikipedia.org/wiki/Albert_Einstein%27s_brain

50 – TheGoan.net, "Think right for those who are left(ies)," October 12, 2019. https://www.thegoan.net/think-right-for-those-who-are-left(ies)/54737.html

51 – Erik Kersten. EscherInHetPaleis.nl, "Left-handedness," August 13, 2019. https://www.escherinhetpaleis.nl/escher-today/left-handedness/?lang=en

52 – Sean Michaels. TheGuardian.com, "Was Jimi Hendrix's ambidexterity the key to his virtuosity?" February 10, 2010. https://www.theguardian.com/music/2010/feb/25/jimi-hendrix-ambidexterity-virtuosity

53 - Andreas Barth. MusicExperience.co.za, "10 Most Famous Left-Handed Musicians," September 17, 2016. https://www.musicexperience.co.za/blogs/news/64316227-10-most-famous-left-handed-musicians

Chapter 2: The Big Three – Da Vinci, Franklin, and Baden-Powell

BADEN-POWELL

1 – Wikipedia.org, "Robert Baden-Powell, 1st Baron Baden-Powell," February 20, 2022. https://wikipedia.org/wiki/Robert_Baden-Powell,_1st_Baron_Baden-Powell

2 – OA-BSA.org, "Lord Baden-Powell," https://oa-bsa.org/history/lord-baden-powell

3 – Scout.org, "Meet Baden-Powell," https://www.scout.org/bp

4 – AtlasObscura.com, "The Founder of the Boy Scouts Hid Maps in Insect Drawings," June 20, 2016.

Dr. Joyce Chaplin, Professor of Early American History at Harvard University, notes that Franklin was "clever with his hands, good at thinking, and hyper-literate" to be able to arrange inverted, mirrored type settings and mirror read them for accuracy.[27] One can conclude that Franklin, who only received two years of elementary education, practiced thousands of hours of mirror reading before retiring from printing at age 42. Soon after, Franklin would make up for his "lack of education" by receiving five honorary degrees, including doctorates from Harvard, Yale, and Oxford universities.[28] Even considering the vast array of things Franklin did and became known for, he still acutely identified with this mirror-reading profession – so much so that he referred to himself in his own will later in life simply as "Benjamin Franklin, Printer."

Many left-handers feel more natural writing mirrored direction (aka right-to-left), such as *the Beatles'* Sir Paul McCartney did as a young child.[29] Did Benjamin Franklin have a left-handed eye for mirror script that gave him a more natural ability to set type faster than competitors? His *Petition of the Left Hand* points out that dual-dominance has excellent benefits. And what does dual-dominance require? A lot of mirror movement!

Let us recall from Chapter 1 how Benjamin Franklin's contemporary, Thomas Jefferson, broke his right wrist in France. Franklin wrote his *Petition* while in France, less than five years before Jefferson arrived.[30] Jefferson and Franklin were together in France for one year before parting ways. Even though Franklin was already back in America when Jefferson broke his wrist, Jefferson may have had knowledge of the *Petition,* inspiring him to further develop his southpaw side more than just did his need of physical rehabilitation. When the two reunited in Philadelphia four years later, in early 1790, I can imagine Franklin sharing with Jefferson his *Petition,* telling him, "Bummer on your wrist, Thomas, but it's no big deal. Both sides are made for EQUAL use, so just keep developing your left hand!"

Figure 2.11: Franklin made many inventions, including Bifocals for better reading

In further connecting Franklin and Jefferson, author Walter Isaacson referred to them both as "Avatars of the Enlightenment."[31] Jefferson also proceeded Franklin as the second U.S. Ambassador to France.

Let us also return for a moment to Franklin's unfinished autobiography, which he wrote between 1771 and 1790, the year he died. It is a work that recalls his life from birth up until 1757, meaning there is still another *22 unaccounted years* before he writes his *Petition* essay in 1779.[32] Perhaps it is within this time period that Franklin dove into a practice of MMD. Or perhaps he practiced MMD to some degree beforehand, but never felt it necessary to mention such details within the busy accounts of political, scientific, economic, philosophical, and civic thoughts he expressed within his autobiography. Or again, perhaps he never practiced MMD at all, outside of mirror reading while setting mirrored type for printing.

Interestingly, Franklin's autobiographical writings arrived at the printer penned in his own, nearly-illegible handwriting.[33] Subsequently, the French publishers, who were the first to print his autobiography, faced extended delays as they struggled to read his awkward scribble. Was this atrocious penmanship due to Franklin working to develop his less-dominant hand or was it just the case of an older man overusing his more-dominant hand? Either sounds

39 – Sarah Pruitt. History.com, "The First Left-handed President Was Ambidextrous and Multilingual", September 1, 2018. https://www.history.com/news/first-left-handed-president-ambidextrous-multilingual

40 – Lucerna Sadhana. RightBrainedHalfHanged.blogspot.com, "Ambidextrous", August 8, 2009. http://rightbrainedhalfhanged.blogspot.com/2009/08/ambidextrous.ht ml

41 – Eddie Deezen. NeatOrama.com, "12 Things You May Not Know About Houdini", October 29, 2014. https://www.neatorama.com/2014/10/29/12-Things-You-May-Not-Know-About-Houdini/

42 – BuzzWorthy.com, "9 Facts You Didn't Know About Illusionist Harry Houdini", 2018. https://www.buzzworthy.com/six-facts-you-didn't-know-about-illusionist-harry-houdini/

43 – Arturo Moser. WikiAboutHoudini.com, "Houdini claimed he was building a "haunted house", February 6, 2016. https://www.wikiabouthoudini.com/2016/02/houdini-claim-that-he-building-haunted-house.html

44 – Chris McManus. Right Hand, Left Hand: The Origins of Asymmetry in Brains, Bodies, Atoms and Chimeres (Orion Publishing, 2003), page 356

45 – David Cracel. SuperMindHacker.com, "Was Albert Einstein Left Or Right Brained? The Shocking Answer", 2020. https://www.supermindhacker.com/was-albert-einstein-left-or-right-brained/

46 – Christopher Bergland. PsychologyToday.com, "Einstein's Genius Linked to Well-Connected Brain Hemispheres", October 5, 2013. https://www.psychologytoday.com/us/blog/the-athletes-linked-well-connected-brain-genius-einsteins/201310/www

47 – Mitch Strohm. Inc.com, "The Scientist Who Studied Einstein's Brain Learned That These 5 Factors Make You Smarter", August 3, 2017. https://www.inc.com/mitch-strohm/what-einsteins-brain-can-tell-us-about-intelligence-a.html

29 – NPS.gov, "Thomas Jefferson," February 11, 2022.
https:\\www.nps.gov\jeff\learn\historyculture\thomas-jefferson.htm

30 – Cristin O'Keefe Aptowicz. SmithsonianMag.com, "Before Dr.
Mutter, Surgery Was a Dangerous and Horrifically Painful Ordeal,"
September 4, 2014. https:\\www.smithsonianmag.com\history\dr-
mutter-surgery-was-dangerous-and-horrifically-painful-ordeal-
180952580\

31 – Matt Blitz. SmithsonianMag.com, "How Einstein's Brain Ended
Up at the Mütter Museum in Philadelphia," April 17, 2015.
https:\\www.smithsonianmag.com\travel\how-einsteins-brain-ended-
mutter-museum-philadelphia-180954987\

32 – Chris McManus. Right Hand, Left Hand: The Origins of Asymmetry
in Brains, Bodies, Atoms and Cultures (Orion Publishing, 2003), page
179

33 – Robert Stacey. ArtMuseum.Utoronto.ca, "Sir Daniel Wilson
(1816–1892): Ambidextrous Polymath," September, 2001.
https:\\artmuseum.utoronto.ca\exhibition\sir-daniel-wilson\

34 – John Jackson. Ambidexterity; Or Two-Handedness and Two-
Brainedness, An Argument For Natural Development And Rational
Education. (Dryden House London, 1905), page 148

35 – Janice Arkatov. LAtimes.com, "Carroll,' Through the Looking
Glass," January 22, 1989. https:\\www.latimes.com\archives\la-xpm-
1989-01-22-ca-110-story.html

36 – Zeena Nackerdien. WordGuru.rocks, "Through the Looking Glass
with Da Vinci and Carroll," 2018. https:\\www.wordguru.rocks\single-
post\2018\07\11\through-the-looking-glass-with-da-vinci-and-carroll

37 – Wikipedia.org, "Ambigram," February 18, 2022.
https:\\wikipedia.org\wiki\Ambigram

38 – Mohammed Noor. WhatsUpLife.in, "Bet you didn't know these
10 Famous people were Ambidextrous," May 31, 2017.
https:\\www.whatsuplife.in\list-famous-ambidextrous-celebs-people-
celebrities

feasible. Considering though that he still lived another 11 years after penning his *Petition*, it would seem odd if Franklin never actually worked during this time to develop both hands, a practice he mentions being so important within the *Petition* essay.

Figure 2.12: Franklin extending his left hand to George Washington in "The Bond" sculpture by Jim West in downtown Philadelphia, Pennsylvania

Whether Franklin passionately practiced MMD is questionable. However, note that Franklin, like Da Vinci and Baden-Powell, exhibited our three hallmarks of a prolific ambidexter:

1. Polymath
2. Luminary who catalyzed human advancements [34]
3. Naturephile who keenly observed the created order, as seen in his love for swimming,[35] charting of the Gulf stream, first proposal of Daylight Savings Time,[36] and applications of electricity [37]

Considering the evidence, one can conclude that Benjamin Franklin practiced a developmental form of MMD during his lifetime.

Leonardo da Vinci

Among polymaths, luminaries, and naturephiles, it's easy to see Leonardo da Vinci as all three. He was an artist, engineer, scientist, theorist, sculptor, and architecture. His personal notebooks are full of insight into anatomy, astronomy, optics, botany, cartography, hydrodynamics, painting, and paleontology.[37]

Figure 2.13: History's quintessential dual-dominant polymath: Leonardo da Vinci

For some, mystery still surrounds the personal, 'secretive' handwriting style of this Italian Renaissance genius. Just like the ancient Greeks with *boustrophedon* and the Easter Islanders with *rongorongo*, Leonardo wrote in both mirrored and inverted script.[38]

Experts from the Opificio delle Pietre Dure, a research and art conservation institute in Florence, Italy, discovered that Leonardo wrote right-handed traditional and left-handed mirrored in his *Landscape* drawing at just 21 years-old.[39] What exactly inspired the young man to work at equally developing both sides of his body via mirrored handwriting? One belief is that Da Vinci switched hands for physical rehabilitation purposes. In one journal entry, Da Vinci thanks God for "having escaped from murderers with only one hand dislocated."[40] Or was Da Vinci inspired by a mentor, teacher, or contemporaries to practice MMD? After all, Leonardo wasn't alone

15 – John Jackson. Ambidexterity; Or Two-Handedness and Two-Brainedness, An Argument For Natural Development And Rational Education. (Dryden House London, 1905), pages 114 & 145

16 – Ibid., pages 114, 117, 135, 154, 157

17 – Ibid., page 128

18 – Ibid., page 114

19 – Wikipedia.org, "Switch pitcher," November 28, 2021. https:\\wikipedia.org\wiki\Switch_pitcher

20 – Chris McManus. Right Hand, Left Hand: The Origins of Asymmetry in Brains, Bodies, Atoms and Cultures (Orion Publishing, 2003), page 364

21 – Wikipedia.org, "Plato," February 20, 2022. https:\\wikipedia.org\wiki\Plato

22 – Luke Mastin. RightLeftRightWrong.com, "History of Handedness – Ancient History," 2012. https:\\www.rightleftrightwrong.com\history_ancient.html

23 – Chris McManus. Right Hand, Left Hand: The Origins of Asymmetry in Brains, Bodies, Atoms and Cultures (Orion Publishing, 2003), page McManus, page 364

24 – Ibid., page 282

25 – Ibid., pages 282-283

26 – Lisa Marder. ThoughtCo.com, "10 Famous Left-Handed Artists: Chance or Destiny," August 27, 2018. https:\\www.thoughtco.com\a-list-of-left-handed-artists-4077979

27 – Andreas Barth. MusicExperience.co.za, "10 Most Famous Left-Handed Musicians," September 17, 2016. https:\\www.musicexperience.co.za\blogs\news\643\6227\-10-most-famous-left-handed-musicians

28 – Christopher Bergland. PsychologyToday.com, "Einstein's Genius Linked to Well-Connected Brain Hemispheres," October 5, 2013. https:\\www.psychologytoday.com\us\blog\the-athletes-way\201310\einsteins-genius-linked-well-connected-brain-hemispheres

3 – IfitTraining.co.uk, "Asymmetry in the Human Body," January 13, 2017. https://www.ifittraining.co.uk/insights/asymmetry-human-body/

4 – Diego Irigoyen. Lettering-Daily.com, "How to Become Ambidextrous in 6 Easy Steps," 2018. https://www.lettering-daily.com/6-steps-to-become-ambidextrous/

5 – TheOTToolbox.com, "Writing with Both Hands – What you Need to Know," April 15, 2019. https://www.theottoolbox.com/writing-with-both-hands-what-you-need/

6 – Jean-Paul Fischer. TheConversation.com, "Understanding children's mirror writing," November 29, 2017. https://theconversation.com/understanding-childrens-mirror-writing-87948

7 – WorldHistoryEdu.com, "5 Great Accomplishments of Ancient Greece," February 27, 2021. https://www.worldhistoryedu.com/great-achievements-of-ancient-greece/

8 – Wikipedia.org, "Ancient Greek," February 13, 2022. https://wikipedia.org/wiki/Ancient_Greek

9 – Wikipedia.org, "Boustrophedon", February 18, 2022. https://wikipedia.org/wiki/Boustrophedon

10 – Igor Chykalov. Medium.com, "Brain and Body Ambidexterity," August 26, 2020. https://medium.com/illumination/brain-and-body-ambidexterity-e6d92ad3cd19

11 – John Jackson. Ambidexterity; Or Two-Handedness and Two-Brainedness, An Argument For Natural Development And Rational Education. (Dryden House London, 1905), pages 143-144

12 – Wikipedia.org, "Rongorongo," February 9, 2022. https://wikipedia.org/wiki/Rongorongo

13 – Warehouse-13-Artifact-Database-Wiki.com, "Leonardo da Vinci's Notebook," https://warehouse-13-artifact-database.fandom.com/wiki/Leonardo_da_Vinci%27s_Notebook

14 – Wikiwand.com, "Mirror writing," February 18, 2022. https://www.wikiwand.com/en/Mirror_writing

among his peers to exhibit dual-dominance. Michelangelo, Raphael, and Dante were also Italian Renaissance creatives known to be ambidextrous.[41]

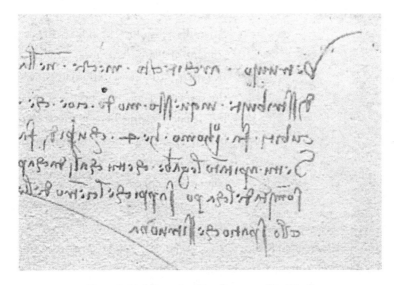

Figure 2.14: Mirrored writing from one of Da Vinci's 7,200+ personal notebook pages

Da Vinci was a keen and curious observer. Based on his meticulous, anatomical drawings of human exterior features, skeletons, muscles, joints, and ligaments – observed while secretly dissecting human cadavers [42] – Da Vinci would have noticed the body's design for symmetric, bilateral movement.[43] As an engineer, he may have noted this symmetry and concluded that no Creator of such an organic *machine* would ever intend for it to move and develop asymmetrically. Thus, Da Vinci would have found it appropriate to adopt the combined practice of mirrored and traditional handwriting, a practice that symmetrically develops the body. In fact, many of his more inventive sketches are full of symmetry, like his *Rhombicuboctahedron* and *Vitruvian Man*.[44] He

38

became obsessed with analyzing the bilateral symmetry that allows birds to fly.[45] Even the earliest drafts of how to build a flying conveyance for humans came from Da Vinci.[46]

Leonardo's love of symmetry may have been partly inspired by

Aristotle, the Greek polymath and student of Plato.[47] Aristotle wrote that *symmetry*, order, and definiteness, were the three chief forms of beauty, proven by science everywhere.[48] It is also believed that Aristotle's observations on underwater acoustics, meteorology, and color perspective inspired Da Vinci.[49]

Figure 2.15: Da Vinci's spatially-pristine rhombicuboctahedron sketch

Considering Leonardo's mirrored handwriting style, some claim he was simply left-handed or dyslexic,[50] even though he penned right-handed traditional whenever writing to someone else.[51] This ability for Da Vinci to equally use both hands can be explained by the fact that less-dominant mirrored handwriting can be developed by any average person, at any age.[52] Remember, humans do not enter the world with an innate ability to read or write, let alone with a 'dominant' hand. Rather, we spend years working to develop it. The same is true for an average adult developing less-dominant mirror writing or mirror reading – with a lot of practice, it can become as natural as the traditional direction.

Thankfully, for the average adult, developing your less-dominant side in mirrored motion takes less time than the initial development of your dominant side. This is because your dominant side works as a seasoned teacher to streamline the process for your less-dominant side when learning the same activity mirrored.[53] One great benefit from this process is that your more-dominant side

2 – Vocabulary.com, Definition 'Ambidextrous,' https://www.vocabulary.com/dictionary/ambidextrous

3 – David Wolman. A Left-Hand Turn Around the World: Chasing the Mystery and Meaning of All Things Southpaw (De Capo Press, 2005), page 15

4 – Jim Houliston. Ambilife.org, "Benefits of MMD," September 24, 2021. https://ambilife.org/benefits-of-mmd/

5 – History.com, "Leonardo da Vinci," December 2, 2009. https://www.history.com/topics/renaissance/leonardo-da-vinci

6 – Leonardo da Vinci, translated by Jean Paul Richter (1888). The Complete Notebooks of Leonardo da Vinci (Eternal Sun Books, 2016), page 22

7 – Adam Sinicki. TheBioneer.com, "Training Ambidexterity – For Athleticism, Creativity, and Symmetry," March 26, 2021. https://www.thebioneer.com/ambidexterity-training/

***The term "Manual transfer learning," is taken from a book I read over two years ago that discusses this same cited concept as "Intermanual Transfer of Skill." Frankly, I have not been able to relocate "manual transfer learning," when reviewing the books I have read, but still prefer this term, so I choose to use it throughout BIG3MMD. I hope to relocate this reference one day and include it in an updated version of BIG3MMD.

Chapter 1: History's Spectrum of MMD

1 – Mario Livio. HuffPost.com, "Why Are We Symmetrical?," December 6, 2017. https://www.huffpost.com/entry/why-are-we-symmetrical_b_1836534

2 – David Wolman. A Left-Hand Turn Around the World: Chasing the Mystery and Meaning of All Things Southpaw (De Capo Press, 2005), page 46

REFERENCES

How to Read a Biscriptal Book

1 – Emma G. Duerden and Daniele Laverdure-Dupont, *NeuroSci.org*, "Practice Makes Cortex," August 27, 2008.
https:\\www.jneurosci.org/content/jneuro/28/35/8655/full.pdf

2 – Michael C. Corballis. Frontiers in Human Neuroscience, "Mirror-Image Equivalence and Interhemispheric Mirror-Image Reversal," April 2018.
https:\\www.researchgate.net/publication/287968292_Interhemispheric_mirror-image_reversal

Disclaimer

1 – David Wolman. *A Left-Hand Turn Around the World; Chasing the Mystery and Meaning of All Things Southpaw* (De Capo Press, 2005), pages 14-15

2 – Chris McManus. *Right Hand, Left Hand; The Origins of Asymmetry in Brains, Bodies, Atoms and Cultures* (Orion Publishing, 2003), pages 329-330

Introduction

1 – Jim Houliston. AmbiLife.org, "Today's MMD Practitioners," September 17, 2021. https:\\ambilife.org/todays-mmd-practitioners\

actually improves when you focus simply on developing your less-dominant side, a concept mentioned earlier as manual transfer learning.[54]

Figure 2.16: Symmetry – one of three chief forms of beauty, according to the Da Vinci-inspiring Aristotle

As a highly skilled embodiment of both art and science, Da Vinci is synonymous with the word 'polymath,' or one who is learned in many subjects. His personal notebooks highlight a mind working in otherworldly overdrive, capable of computing more on various topics than the average brain. 19th-century transcribers of Da Vinci's writings even commented that many of his entries can only be understood by specialists of corresponding disciplines, whether Physics, Mechanics, Biology, etc.[55] Interestingly, like Benjamin Franklin, Da Vinci lacked years of formal education.[56]

Da Vinci's practice of dual-directional handwriting not only equally balances the micro muscles of the hands and bilateral posture of the body, but also fosters brain growth.[57] If it's true that MMD grows the brain and its capacity for computative, observational power, then Leonardo manifests the heights of practice.

In addition to mirrored direction, why did Da Vinci invert his handwriting? When addressing this, it's important to note that Leonardo was the first person to understand that the human eye performs as a *camera obscura* – inverting an image within the back of the eye before the brain reverts it again.[58] This discovery may have compelled Leonardo to invert his writing as an exercise for increasing spatial awareness and better understanding our connection within the natural order.[59] Observing nature was an obvious passion of Da

Vinci's considering the exhaustive detail in which he wrote about light, shadow, human form, water, air, botany, mechanics, and more. He even considered the job of a painter as to "imitate all the works of *Nature* which adorn the world."[60]

While Da Vinci was certainly curious, intelligent, disciplined,

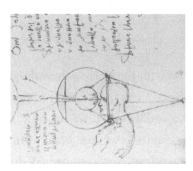

Figure 2.17: Da Vinci's discovery of the eyeball as a camera obscura

and talented, it is arguably his uncommon sense of spatial awareness that best defines him. How much of this ability, though, was he born with? How much of it did he actually work to develop? I am not alone in believing that Leonardo's choice to develop traditional, mirrored, and inverted handwriting is what shaped much of his mind to observe and articulate the world as he did.

Diego Irigoyen, one of the best mirror and inverted writers I know today, shares in his book, *Creative Brain Training: Increase Attention Span, Build Confidence, and Stimulate Creativity,* the belief that much of Leonardo's genius was nurtured through his practice of mirror writing.[61] Da Vinci even considered mirrors as the master of painters, saying, "the mind of the painter must resemble a mirror" and that "*the mirror is our teacher,* giving us a fresh eye."[62]

Jim's additional interests include:

- Seeing the U.S. end the War on Drugs, invest more money in drug abuse prevention, education, and rehabilitation, and help turn Latin America into the secure and thriving region it deserves to be.
- Seeing people suffering from Church-related Anxiety Disorder (C-RAD) have adequate and honest community within the contemporary church scene.
- Sharing his thoughts on fixing the world's problems and what the "end times" may look like.

A fun day for Jim includes long-distance longboarding, rail walking, ambiball, inversions, chalk art, ping pong dancing, skate yoga, backwards walking, and enjoying craft beer with friends.

ABOUT THE AUTHOR

Chalking it up at 13th & Chestnut in Downtown Philly

Jim Houliston is a Philadelphia-based, dual-dominant artist, athlete, educator, and author of the world's first modern biscriptal book – BIG3MMD: History's Ambidextrous and the Benefits of Mirror Movement Development. He grew up in Old Forge, Pennsylvania, received his B.A. in Communication Studies from West Chester University of PA, and spent 14 years living between San Diego, California and Tijuana and Guadalajara, Mexico...Órale!

His next work is to facilitate a community of MMD practitioners, create and promote MMD products, and publish another biscriptal book – one about today's ambidextrous. Learn more at AmbiLife.org.

In summary, there is nothing within the mechanical design of our human body that limits it to writing – or performing any other lateral activity – with just one hand. The only way to become proficient at mirrored movement is through practice. As a 10-year MMD practitioner who has experienced subsequent body realignment and increased brain efficiency, it is clear to me that Leonardo da Vinci filled the 7,200+ pages of his personal notebooks with mirrored and inverted handwriting for three reasons:[63]

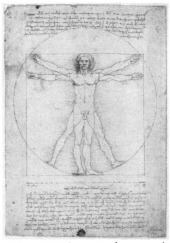

Figure 2.18: Symmetry, beauty, and mirrored writing in Da Vinci's sketch of the Vitruvian Man

1. To symmetrically exercise his brain and body,
2. Increase spatial awareness, and
3. Honor his organic-mechanical design for equal, bilateral movement.

As a sidenote, one of Da Vinci's notebooks – the 72-page *Codex Leicester* – is the most expensive book in the world. It was bought at auction for $30 million dollars by Bill Gates, who has toured it around the world to educate people on the insights and achievements of Da Vinci...[64]

Mr. Gates, if you're reading this (I know you read a lot of books), please make a feature on Microsoft products that mirror images everything on our screens. This way, we can all practice mirror reading and become more brilliant like Leonardo. Thanks, Bill!

My personal coach, Daniel Vázquez Montaño, for all the advice, tools, and encouragement to work hard and push through to make this book a reality.

My friends and neighbors, Simón Gutkin, Cat Valverde, Brad Morris, Miguel Rodríguez, Kenny Donohue, Katie Butler, Seth Goldenberg, and Sebastian Reyes, for giving me great additional content and for receiving my many months of mental/verbal processing while putting this book together.

Dave Srebro and the Northeastern PA Council of the Boy Scouts of America for all the great years of left-handed handshakes, square knot-tying, and lessons learned about Baden-Powell.

Dr. Shelagh Robinson for her work in bringing mirror reading to the masses through her research and creation of MirrorRead.com.

Dr. V.S. Ramachandran for his work in developing mirror therapy and for what it has done to help my friend, Timmy Gretz.

Philadelphia's Parkway Central Library and the University of Pennsylvania's Van Pelt-Dietrich Library for accommodating me over the many hours I spent there researching and writing for this book.

ACKNOWLEDGMENTS

Thanks to...

My childhood friend, **Timmy Gretz**, for inadvertently teaching me more about the human brain than anyone. I am always sorry about your accident, but it has shown me just how important that squishy, 3-pound organ/machine inside our head really is and what it is more capable of accomplishing through MMD.

My fellow 'right-handed', lefty-learning ambidexters: **Ebiye Jeremy, Dr. Kathryn Ko, Diego Irigoyen, and Michael J. Lavery**. Your stories have inspired me to share my own. And just like all of you, I am excited to see lots of people join our ambitribe and benefit greatly from practicing MMD.

My left-handed Editor and Aunt, **Patricia Wallace**, for her hard work in making the most sense of my writing. Incidentally, she was a natural mirror writer as a young child.

My gringo amigo, **David Reisman**, and fellow Seton Catholic High School Alumni, **Maria Recupero English and Richard Mogavero**, for insight and editorial assistance.

My *Frienemy*, **Adam Jones**, for kicking my butt into making this book cover better than the "rave card," it was originally going to look like.

CHAPTER 3
The Science of MMD

The most powerful organ in your body is also the most intelligent 'machine' of all time – our human brain.[1] At just 3 pounds in the average adult, the human brain comprises only 2% of total body weight,[2] but consumes a whopping 20% of the body's energy supply.[3]

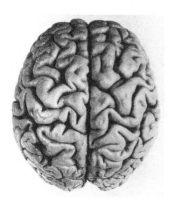

The historic individuals featured in *BIG3MMD* possessed brains that could be considered efficient and well-developed. But how much of this reality has to do with their practice of MMD? What *exactly* does MMD do to the brain?

Figure 3.1: Like our asymmetrically-placed internal organs, the brain performs different functions within the bilateral hemispheres. As far as body movement goes, though, the brain is designed for achieving symmetric performance

Although some estimates say only 1% of the global population is dual-dominant,[4] how many people do you know intentionally work to develop both sides of their body in all activities? I bet it's currently still far less than 1%. And of those people, how many have been extensively researched? Considering how piecemeal and

45

In writing BIG3MMD, my goal has been greater than just presenting to you information on the history and science of MMD; I want to inspire you to adopt the MMD lifestyle and experience the benefits for yourself!

MMD may be the greatest missing piece of basic human development and primary education in our world. Imagine the state of this planet if we all developed our brains and bodies according to their design for equal bilateral movement. We would become collectively greater than all the polymaths, luminaries, and naturephiles listed in this book. What a great world that would be!

So, are you ready to practice MMD? You can start today! Ambidexters are self-taught by the greatest teacher: their own bilateral sides, focusing first on less-dominant mirrored movement. No additional coach is needed to begin and continue MMD, although insight can always be gained from masters of the practice. Visit AmbiLife.org for more information on MMD, to get tips from advanced practitioners, and to join the MMD community.

CONCLUSION

The average human body is mechanically designed for equal bilateral movement (aka MMD), just like a car is mechanically designed for equal left and right turns. Our brain and body receives incredible benefit when engaged in MMD. So, let's treat our bodies according to their natural design by practicing MMD!

Remember, start small and allow your body and brain the time needed to rest, recuperate, and grow from the lifestyle practice of MMD. While young children instinctively practice MMD, it can take adult practitioners years before experiencing fluency. But don't give up! Every adult I know who practices MMD says it is the best choice they have ever made for their mental and physical well-being.

MMD produces many benefits, including body realignment, high-precision balance, brain efficiency, weight-loss, increased memory, heightened spatial awareness, physical longevity, and more.

So, what do you think? Is MMD worth spending the time and effort to practice for achieving physical rehabilitation goals, peak performance, and an optimal, creative neurological state?

We read of famous luminaries, polymaths, and naturephiles who historically practiced a spectrum of MMD. Do you believe MMD was responsible for making distinctive brain changes that helped create their uniqueness? Do these MMD-related qualities intrigue you?

anecdotal much of the research has been on dual-dominance, there's room for improvement when understanding the science and nature behind it. Even Dr. Richard Palmer, Professor of Biology at the University of Alberta, admits that the amount we know with confidence about human handedness is so pitiful it's almost shocking.[5]

In developing this chapter, I researched information related to "the science and benefits of developing ambidexterity." Not one article I found said, "Newsflash: Humans are designed for MMD and everyone can benefit from its practice!" Instead, most articles remarked how little we still know about neuroscience,[6] debated the origin – and even definition – of handedness,[7] and drew correlations between handedness and brain lateralization (e.g. language, memory, and other functions residing within different cerebral hemispheres).[8] Some of the articles even claim that developing ambidexterity has negative side effects, leading to ADHD, schizophrenia and other mental disorders.[9]

Figure 3.2: Symmetric exterior features are designed for equal, bilateral mirrored movement

This may be where MMD and cultural ambidexterity differ. Cultural ambidexterity teaches reading and writing with both hands in one, traditional direction. MMD, on the other hand (quite literally, the other hand), teaches reading and writing with both hands in two directions – mirrored and traditional. While benefit certainly comes from physically exercising both hands in a micro-muscular fashion, the practice of using both brain hemispheres to communicate the action of writing in one, unilateral direction may be confusing to spatial recognition portions of our bilateral brain – an organ designed for mirror processing movement between, both, the left and right mirrored sides of our body.[10]

By this point, I had to remember that this chapter on the science of MMD is being presented backwards; I am not

Figure 3.3: Our design for mirrored movement permits developing dual-dominance through practice

a unidextrous scientist studying others to see if this all *may* be true. Rather, I am a dual-dominant, 10-year-practicing, MMD "guinea pig" who is sharing with you the beautiful results I have personally *experienced* to be true along this journey. Even though I know firsthand that dual-dominance can be developed by the average person and that the benefits are amazing, I want to better understand the science behind *why* and present the information I have found.

Remember, you can also hear from some of today's foremost MMD practitioners at *AmbiLife.org*. Like me, they claim that working to develop dual-dominance is one of the greatest choices they have ever made, and advocate the practice for others.

Taking all this into account, it is important to remember three things regarding our approach to understanding the science behind MMD...

First, **globally, we are using our unilaterally-developed brains to try understanding how the bilaterally-designed brain works.** If our own bilateral brains are not more equally formed through the practice of MMD, are we truly capable of understanding how MMD is supposed to work and be experienced? Before practicing MMD for physical rehabilitation from skateboarding, I never considered ambidexterity as a learnable ability.[11] I had only ever heard of people

incorporate to practice mirror reading:

- **Software programs like Adobe Acrobat and PDF-XChange** allow you to mirror image PDF documents, making it easy to print and read mirrored hard copies.
- **Smart phone editing features** make it possible to horizontally flip photos and screenshots of text into mirrored images.
- Lastly, there's the traditional, **reading-in-a-mirror technique.** To mirror read from my Android phone while going to bed or lying down at a park, I can rest my cell phone on my chest and chin, pointed upwards at a small, hand-held mirror, and read into the mirror. You can also do the same while seated upright using a mirror angled at 45 degrees parallel to the phone.

being *born* ambidextrous (aka dual-dominant). It was only until after working hard to make a habit of practicing lifestyle MMD that I realized dual-dominance could even be developed as an adult.

Second, **most of us only ever use whatever hand, foot, or stance feels most comfortable.** If we only ever do whatever is most comfortable, it would mean rarely practicing disciplines like exercise and healthy eating. We all know the results such a lack of discipline can produce. Developing less-dominant handedness, as connected to brain and body development, is a comparable discipline, but has been practiced much less among cultures for millennia. As a result, this lack of natural, bilateral development has been an unquestionably acceptable norm for most years of humanity on Earth – even though we can each see a bilateral human being designed for symmetric movement staring back at us every time we look in the mirror. This short cutting of our intended development has led to a unilateral design of the human-centric world. As a result, practicing MMD may be difficult to fathom for many of us since there are certain activities and movements we have never performed switch before. For example:

- No car on Earth has its brake pedal on the right and gas pedal on the left [12]
- Most people have never driven a car with the steering wheel on the right side and console features to their left
- There does not yet exist a truly mirrored computer keyboard
- No pair of mass-produced jeans exists with the "fifth pocket" on the left side
- 99.999+% of text you have ever read has been in the traditional direction
- Baseball players never run clockwise around bases

- Clocks are still only read *clockwise*
- Screws are designed to be more easily tightened by the right hand, using the more powerful supination forearm muscles, as opposed to the weaker pronation muscles [13]
- The vast majority of corkscrews, can openers, microwaves, credit card machines, gas pumps, twist-off bottle caps, watches, spiral notebooks, ladles, measuring cups, desks, scissors, and computer mice are just some of the many items that are designed exclusively for the right hand [14]

As you can see, we have collectively made it difficult to practice many forms of MMD. This has led to producing very few advanced MMD practitioners who can be widely studied.

Figure 3.4: Children tend to use both hands before adults tell them to focus on just one

Third, **young children tend to instinctively switch hands between tasks and, periodically, write mirror-style.**[15] It seems as if their unadulterated bodies internally know they are designed for MMD. In relation to training his own children to develop ambidexterity, *Whole Brain Power* author, Michael J. Lavery says, "I feel strongly that there were no negative ramifications from overriding my kids' natural predisposition to favoring one limb over the other."[16]

Your less-dominant hand is connected to a highly functional brain, which can learn many skilled activities, if motivated.[17] The layman's science behind MMD is simple: Moving the right side of your body exercises the left-brain hemisphere, while moving the left side of your body exercises the right-brain hemisphere.[18] The brain starting to illuminate the dynamics of neuroplasticity that occur when we read mirrored text."[7]

MRI brain scan research shows that mirror reading stimulates gray matter growth in right-brain cortex regions not associated with traditional reading.[8] Mirror reading is linked to mental rotation, working memory, procedural memory, and spatial transformation.[9] In other words, neurons fire into both brain hemispheres when you practice mirror reading!

As you practice reading the mirrored portion of BIG3MMD, you will immediately notice that it's harder to read than the traditional direction. Just like your less-dominant hand or foot acclimating over time to general mirrored activity, the less-dominant side of your bilateral brain needs time to acclimate to mirror reading. Like all MMD, mirror reading is a beneficial practice that gets easier over time and brings your body and brain into a more aligned, optimal state.

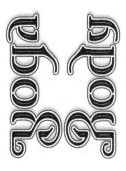

Figure 5.3: "Yoga Body," mirrored vertical ambigram

Tools and Techniques

In addition to the MirrorRead.com web browser tool and app, there are a few other tools and methods you can

ELEVEN SYMMETRIC LETTERS
IN THE ENGLISH ALPHABET

A
H
I
M
V
O
W
T
U
X
Y

Figure 5.4: 11 of 26 letters in the English alphabet are identical when visual mirrored or traditionally

learned through practice over time. What happens then to the brain and body when you choose to "flip the script," and work at learning to read and write in mirrored direction?

Mirror reading is an MMD exercise that produces multiple, science-based benefits. We can understand much of this thanks to **Dr. Shelagh Robinson, Ph.D.**, a professor of Psychology at Dawson College in Montreal, Canada and Founder of Mirror Read, Inc. Her specialized work and research in Visual Perception shows how mirror reading contributes to brain enhancement.

Dr. Robinson started Mirror Read, Inc. in 2010 after spending nearly 20 years practicing mirror writing.[3] Her inspiration came from Leonardo da Vinci and Lewis Carroll, two of history's most famous mirror writers. Mirror Read, Inc. produces mirror-image books and digital games for kids, read right-to-left, for research, educational, and entertainment purposes.

MirrorRead.com features an iPhone app and web-browser tool that mirror rotates everything on your screen, allowing you to practice mirror reading without needing a physical mirror.

Figure 5.2: Dr. Shelagh Robinson created Mirror Read, Inc. to share the mental benefits of mirror reading

According to Dr. Robinson, mirror reading is a complex cognitive skill studied by researchers across the globe.[4] Scientists use mirror-reversed text to measure spatial rotation skills[5] and test procedural memory in Alzheimer's and Huntington's patients.[6] Dr. Robinson says the real mysteries of mirror reading lie at the level of the neuron, chemistry, and electrics of learning: "We are only

hemispheres, like all other bilateral muscles, can be equally challenged through the practice of MMD. Neuroscience can now quantify these brain changes with brain scans.[19]

The hands communicate information to the brain as surely as the brain communicates information to the hands,[20] having co-evolved together.[21] As a result, our hands use nearly 25% of the brain's *motor strip* processing power.[22]

We can develop dual-dominance thanks to our brain's rewiring capabilities, known as *neuroplasticity* or *neurogenesis*. Your brain can grow new cells and create new connections as it works to learn mirrored movements.[23] These new brain neurons can be formed at any age.[24]

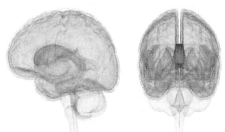

Figure 3.5: Shaded view of the Corpus Callosum at the center of the brain

50% of all brain neurons are located inside the *cerebellum,* which comprises just 10% of the brain's mass. This cerebellum controls posture, muscle movement, and stores memories for modifying motor function.[25]

When your body is engaged in equal, bilateral exercise, *blood* flows to both sides of the brain.[26] This blood flow provides *oxygen* that grows *new neurons* and *synapses* within in the *cerebral cortex, motor strip*, and *hippocampus*. This also thickens your brains' *corpus callosum* – the fibrous "communication bridge" at the center of your brain and crossing point of all bilateral activity.[27]

Single-sided body development leads to a smaller corpus callosum.[28] On average, women have a larger corpus callosum than men[29] and process language more evenly between brain hemispheres.[30] The corpus callosum is also 11% larger in most lefties, due to a need of using their less-dominant right hand to operate right hand-designed tools, machines, and objects.[31]

Though there appears to be correlation, science is still not conclusive that right-handed people are left-brain dominant and left-handed people right-brain dominant.[32] Sadly, left-handers are often excluded from neurological research due to the average greater physical difference in their brains, namely that *their brains are more symmetric* than those of right-handers.[33] When it comes to genetics, some scientists even believe there is a gene for right-handedness, but no gene for left-handedness.[34]

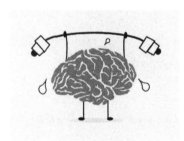

Figure 3.6: MMD is a major workout for your brain

Two great books that discuss the science of MMD using personal case studies from MMD practitioners are *Whole Brain Power*, by Michael J. Lavery, and *Creative Brain Training*, by Diego Irigoyen. Their findings conclude that MMD causes:

- Neurons to activate in the opposite *temporal lobe,* aiding in the development of *spatial intelligence* [35]
- The *corpus callosum* to thicken and the *cerebral cortex, motor strip, and hippocampus* to stimulate [36]
- Increased skill development by exponentially improving one side of the body, then the other side, and back again [37]

CHAPTER 5

Mirror Reading

The chosen direction of written languages is arbitrary.[1] Some scripts traditionally go right-to-left, others left-to-right. Some go vertical. Written languages can be character-based, use letters, or whatever else a culture decides makes sense. Like the majority of world scripts, English has held a left-to-right standard – the writing direction best suited for a right hand.[2]

Figure 5.1: "DreamMagic" cutout mirrored ambigram

Regardless of the directionality a culture chooses for its scripted language, the ability to read and write it is something that no one on Earth is innately born with. Rather, the ability to read and write is

- *Neurogenesis, myelination, glucose consumption,* and *blood flow* in both brain hemispheres [38]
- *Endosteroidogenesis* (the natural, internal creation of *bodily steroids*), producing *pregnenolone, DHEA, testosterone, estradiol, estrogen,* and *progesterone.* This protects the cellular structures in the *dentate gyrus,* which is where *new memory cells* are formed inside the *hippocampi* [39]
- The *pre-frontal* and *frontal lobes* to become nourished through sustained beta brainwave activity, creating *a cascade of chemical reactions,* resulting in the production of *adenosine triphosphate* (ATP) [40]

Hemispheric Recognition of Language

The cerebral center for processing language, known as *Broca's area,* is found in the left-brain hemisphere of nearly 97% of humanity.[41] This makes sense considering most of us, including our ancestors from whom we get our genes, have been using the right hand to write for thousands of years.[42] So, what would have happened if our ancestors chose a more balanced handwriting style, alternating between both hands in mirrored and traditional directions, in line with our symmetric, bilateral design? Would we have two *Broca's areas* between both hemispheres?

One day in early 2021, I was on the phone with my aunt Dara during a drive from Scranton, Pennsylvania, to Philadelphia. While chatting on my headset, Dara tells me of a new cuisine style she had been experimenting with cooking. It was a cuisine I never heard of before, so I asked her to spell it out. As she did, I instinctively raised my left hand, sounded out the letters, air wrote each letter in mirrored direction, and saw the mirrored word in my minds' eye! I immediately told Dara this was the first time that had ever happened. Operating subconsciously from my traditionally 'less-dominant' side in mirrored direction was exciting. This occurred after more than one year of mirrored reading and writing.

Does this mean that my left-hemisphered Broca's area has now shifted to the right hemisphere? Considering that I am still just as good at writing in the traditional direction with my right hand, my already-developed Broca's area should still be the same, if not better. Perhaps my Broca's area is in the process of duplicating itself onto the right-brain hemisphere and becoming more solidified every time I practice left-handed mirror writing.

Michael J. Lavery reports that his students, after *just a few weeks* of practicing less-dominant mirrored handwriting, say their dominant hand is working and writing better than ever, and their mirror writing is slowing beginning to look like their dominant writing.[43] In fact, most righties are surprised at how easy it is to write left-handed mirror on a blackboard if their right hand is writing in the traditional direction simultaneously. This can be explained by the fact that the brain hemisphere controlling this movement of the left hand is a mirror-image of the brain hemisphere controlling the right hand.[44]

Mirror Therapy

An MMD exercise worth noting for its scientific intrigue is *mirror box therapy*.[45] Developed by **Dr. V. S. Ramachandran**, Neuroscientist and Director of the *Center for Brain and Cognition* at the University of Southern California, San Diego, mirror box therapy treats amputees suffering from phantom limb pain. The concept is simple: a mirror is positioned inside an open-ended box

NHL player, using a straight-bladed stick to switch stances between both sides.[33]

65-year-old golfer, Norman White, after surgery to his right shoulder, began focusing more on his less-dominant left side. Today, after years of practice, he plays exclusively switch and recently sunk his first switch hole-in-one. His only other hole-in-one happened 15 years earlier, while playing righty. After more than 40 years of playing golf, Norman says his best years are still ahead of him.[34]

Like Norman, it was through seeking physical rehabilitation that I discovered MMD. My 10 years of exclusive, single-sided skateboarding could not be balanced out by repeated chiropractor visits. It was only by switching over to my less-dominant side and continuing to skate accordingly that my body was able to realign itself. Not only have I now been skateboarding for more than 25 years – and see no end in sight – but I have gained new abilities, my body feels better than ever, and I'm having more fun!

It is abundantly clear: the human body is made for MMD.

human body is connected.[28] The same can be said for asymmetries. If your right shoulder is stronger than your left, or the left side of your hip is tighter than the right, compensatory patterns will occur. The two biggest precursors to injury are asymmetries and previous injury.[29] Chronic injuries that inhibit most athletes are, usually, associated with the overuse of one side of the body. When athletes equally use both sides, though, propensity for injury decreases, the body balances out, and longevity increases.[30] By comparing and contrasting the movements of each side, your body borrows intelligence from the dominant side to educate your less-dominant side. This minimizes movement deficiencies and improves overall athletic capacity, balance, coordination, and strength, leading to longevity.

An online search of workouts associated with longevity consistently mentions six activities: walking, swimming, cycling, running, yoga, and tennis.[31] Five of these six activities are symmetric with tennis being the exception, unless you play it MMD-style like former Grand Slam doubles champion, Luke "Dual Hand" Jensen. As the former head tennis coach of Syracuse University, Jensen trained his student athletes to serve ambidextrously, a skill that most players picked up in as little as two months.[32]

Figure 4.5: NHL legend, Gordie Howe, was the most dual-dominant player and played more seasons than anyone

Ice hockey legend, Gordie Howe, at 26 seasons through five decades, spent more time in the NHL than anyone, even playing on the same team as his two sons. He was also the best dual-dominant

that is then put in place of a missing limb from an amputee. With this method, instead of viewing the area of a missing limb, an amputee now *sees* a moving limb – the mirrored image of their intact side. The mirrored image moving fluidly *visually* convinces their brain that the once-missing limb is now whole again.[46]

Figure 3.7: Patient using mirror therapy

I tried this technique with my childhood friend, Timmy Gretz, who suffers from left-sided mobility issues caused by a right-sided traumatic brain injury (TBI). Placing a wall mirror between his less-mobile left side and torso, I had Timmy look into the mirror as he worked to raise both arms together. Timmy, who could not see his left arm since it was now being hidden by the mirror, was able to raise his left arm notably higher than before, thanks to help from the mirror!

Figure 3.8: Always excited to hang with my childhood friend, Timmy Gretz

During mirror box therapy, a portion of Timmy's brain is visually convinced that his disabled left arm is now equal with his capable right arm. As one of our five senses, one would think that *sight* composes 20% of total sensory recognition, but it is actually closer to 85%.[47] If this 85% can be 100% convinced that what it sees is completely 'normal', respective mental energy becomes available to help improve sensory mobility.

The ability to imagine and visualize is a powerful tool for achieving goals. In fact, many top athletes talk about the power of visualization as one of their keys to success.[48] Even Albert Einstein said, "Imagination is more important than knowledge."[49]

We will return to more on the science of MMD within the upcoming section on *Mirror Reading*.

them a few years ago. More importantly, it makes me excited to discover new additional things that my MMD-trained body can now perform.[26]

With my improved balance and routine of practicing inversions, I can now do better handstands than ever before. With the ability to now write with either hand, I can do larger chalk drawings than ever before. With the ability to now throw with both hands, I can play wallball for longer, and with more movement variety, than ever before. The same goes for kicking a soccer ball, juggling, ping pong, dancing, stretching, and other skills\activities that I learned only within the last few years. And take my word for it: it is exhilarating! The only downside has been finding peers on my same skill level to join in the fun.

Longevity:

Unless you make an equal amount of left and right turns over the lifetime of driving your car, your tires need periodic rotation to maximize their longevity. Of course, you can't rotate your human appendages like rotating car tires, but you can choose to exercise both sides of your bilateral body equally. Does the machine of your human body, with its bilateral structure, work optimally for symmetric movement the same as a car? Is functional longevity increased by exercising both sides of your bilateral body equally?

Training one side of your body more than the other leads to imbalances and decreased longevity.[27] This often results in postural problems and various ailments to soft tissue and ligaments that can be avoided with some balancing out.

The mapping of whole body fascial and myofascial linkages, known as *Thomas Myers' Anatomy Trains*, shows that the entire

Creativity in Art and Concept Development:

Figure 4.4: Art and concept development seen in Benjamin Franklin's symmetric design of 13 rings representing the original British American colonies. Printed on colonial U.S. currency

Dr. Kathryn Ko, a Manhattan-based Neurosurgeon and Fine Artist, believes that her development of ambidexterity while in medical school helped her become a fine artist after already becoming a neurosurgeon. "You need somewhere to focus that extra brain power," says Dr. Ko in relation to the polymathic tendency ambidexters have of adopting a wider spectrum of disciplines.[23]

Creative breakthrough is increased by 60% when engaged in the aerobic MMD activity of walking.[24] In fact, Einstein had the idea for his famous $E=MC^2$ equation while performing another aerobic MMD activity: riding his bike.[25]

New Movement Ability:

After years of practicing MMD, I can now do lots of new things, two of which seem trivial:

1) Separating my left pinky toe from the ring toe, and
2) Rolling my tongue counter-clockwise

As someone who could never do these two simple movements growing up, I could not believe the moment I was first able to do

CHAPTER 4
The Benefits of MMD

You may be thinking, "I already have one good hand. Why need another?" Having an extra, equally strong hand on a rainy day sounds like a nice perk, but the benefits of MMD are much greater than just that.

MMD symmetrically *grows the brain*[1] and *aligns the body*.[2] This leads to some astonishing benefits, including:

- High-precision balance
- Neuro- and synaptogenesis
- Heightened spatial awareness
- Improved memory recollection
- Creativity in art and concept development
- Increased athletic, musical, and fine motor skills[3]
- Increased reaction time and hand-eye coordination
- Endosteroidogenesis (natural, internal creation of steroids)
- Prevention/Onset delay of Alzheimer's disease[4]
- New movement ability
- Increased longevity
- Weight loss

practicing MMD for just three months, shares how he and his students were more physically hungry when working to develop dual-dominance.[18] He reports that up to a 40% caloric intake was being consumed through the brain when practicing MMD.[19] This burn manifest itself in at least two areas:

1. **New neural development:** People often describe a "weird, awkward feeling" when practicing MMD, especially in the beginning stages. That challenging, difficult feeling is your brain physically working to create new neural pathways needed to perform your less-dominant, mirrored movements.[20] Creating these pathways requires energy, which comes from food consumption and/or burning energy stored as fat within the body.

2. **Increased muscle development:** The dual-dominant Olympic Handball player, Ebiye Jeremy Udo-Udoma, says that if the average handball player fatigues after 100 throws in a training session, he fatigues after 150. This is because Ebiye can throw 75 times with his dominant hand and 75 times with his less-dominant hand, meaning each arm feel less fatigued, while simultaneously producing more repetitions. As a result, Ebiye can throw for longer periods of time and burn more calories.[21]

Personally, I now experience the same sense of extended endurance with longboarding. The ability to push equally with both legs allows me to skate longer than ever before. Considering that 15 years ago I had to stop skateboarding entirely after just 10 years of exclusive, unilateral practice of the sport had completely wrecked my body, I see this ability today as remarkable.[22]

endosteroidogenesis in his book, Whole Brain Power. The most interesting study is that of Chuck Mellick.[15] At 38 years old, Mellick aspired to be the first baseball pitcher in history to throw 90 MPH with both his right and left hands. While practicing Lavery's MMD routines, Mellick reported seeing and feeling results that caused him to "eat like a horse," just to maintain his body weight. He even went through a growth spurt, needing a larger hat, shoe, and ring size! Lavery theorizes that his ambidextrous, golf-ball-bouncing, dual-sledgehammer drills forced Mellick's central and peripheral nervous systems to intensely myelinate axon sheaths.[16] In turn, this accommodates the body with a new level of ability to perform such activity. Lavery's research indicates that this myelination produces unique chemical interactions, leading to the internal, natural synthesis of steroids (aka, endosteroidogenesis).

By this point, Mellick's story was getting picked up by various San Francisco Bay Area reporters, including a CBS affiliate. Before airing the story though, the station discussed this claim of endosteroidogenesis with the local medical community, who responded that it is impossible for a 38-year-old man to be experiencing such changes in his body without taking anabolic steroids. As a result of the controversy, Mellick's story never aired.[17]

Weight Loss:

The average person's brain burns 20% of the body's energy. MMD increases this burn. Creative Brain Training author, Diego Irigoyen, who experienced greater attention span, memory recollection, and energy after

Figure 4.3: MMD burns more calories, increasing weight loss

Let's dive into some of my favorites from this list...

Memory Recollection:

Just as communication is vitally important in our day-to-day lives, our two brain hemispheres have a similar relationship regarding memory development. Memories are encoded in the left hemisphere and retrieved in the right.[5] People with greater communication between the hemispheres, identified by mixed-handedness and ambidexterity, show greater memory recollection.[6] Since

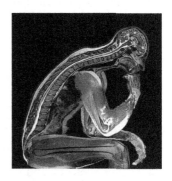

Figure 4.1: Memory recollection increases with MMD

MMD increases cross-hemispheric communication, the ability to recall memories increases.[7] Names, alphanumeric patterns, dates, details, etc. become easier to remember with regular MMD practice, a reality that has been known by brain specialists for centuries.[8]

Reaction Time

The habit of choosing your less-dominant side in all activities increases your reaction time. This is because you now have two sets of trained appendages from which to meet a situation. A great example of this is when you unexpectedly need to catch a falling object. The uni-dominant person needs to know how to get their dominant hand positioned just in time to catch the object or risk trying to use their less-dominant hand, if that's the closer one. But the dual-dominant person can react with less effort since they have two trained hands. Since I grew up not having this ability, I can describe it today as, "getting there *before you get there,*" like a sort of Marvel Comics' *Spidey-sense.*

This can also translate to having an edge in sports, considering one of baseball's all-time best hitters was also one of the best switch hitters: Mickey Mantle.[9]

Spatial Awareness:

Spatial awareness is an organized understanding of objects in space around us. When viewing Da Vinci's abilities, his spatial awareness is considered the most defining.[10] It is best seen in his art, engineering, sketches, and various handwriting directions, including mirrored, inverted, and traditional. If you can better understand the bilateral movement of your body, you can better understand your bilateral body's relationship to the space around it.

MMD has caused me to fall more in love with symmetry and alternative spatial expression. This can be seen in my chalk art and photography. I also instinctively started doing lots of normal activities differently once advancing in MMD. For example, when peeling oranges, I now shape them into different forms, such as stars, zig zags, and spirals. When playing the block tower game *Jenga,* I make symmetric 'X's' all the way up. I also now love walking backwards, frontpacking (aka, front-placed backpacking), ping pong dancing, and handstand/monkey bar inversions, all of which is great for improving posture.

High-Precision Balance:

Developing equal, mirrored movements of your appendages, on both a micro (e.g., handwriting) and macro (e.g., throwing\kicking) scale, fine-tunes the mechanics and major muscle groups of your body, aligning everything toward the center of your spine.[11] This produces uncanny, physical balance.[12]

I experience this best with rail walking.[13] The thought of walking down handrails never occurred to me until I was 35-years-old. Since then, I have learned to walk handrails backwards, over gaps, and with 360° rotations. I encourage rail walking to only be done on round rails. It is important to start small and know your risks and limitations, as you don't want to get injured. Round-rail walking is the most symmetric activity I know. The fine, straight line on top of any firm, round rail

Figure 4.2: A 36-stair handrail walk requires a bit of balance

ensures that your body equally exercises both lateral sides in order to maintain balance. After a rail walking session, I often feel refreshingly aligned, like having just visited a chiropractor.

Endosteroidogenesis:

MMD naturally produces steroids within your body.[14] Michael J. Lavery, who has over 25 years of experience in teaching dual-dominance, includes some interesting case studies on this concept of

60

TWO THINGS GOD WANTED
FOR HUMANITY WERE
PERFECTION AND IMMORTALITY...

AT LEAST HE GOT THE THIRD:
FREEDOM.

High-Precision Balance:

Developing equal, mirrored movements of your appendages, on both a micro (e.g., handwriting) and macro (e.g., throwing/kicking) scale, fine-tunes the mechanics and major muscle groups of your body, aligning everything toward the center of your spine.[11] This produces uncanny, physical balance.[12]

Figure 4.2: A 36-stair handrail walk requires a bit of balance

I experience this best with rail walking.[13] The thought of walking down handrails never occurred to me until I was 35 years-old. Since then, I have learned to walk handrails backwards, over gaps, and with 360° rotations. I encourage rail walking to only be done on *round* rails. It is important to start small and know your risks and limitations, as you don't want to get injured. Round-rail walking is the most symmetric activity I know. The fine, straight line on top of any firm, round rail ensures that your body equally exercises both lateral sides in order to maintain balance. After a rail walking session, I often feel refreshingly aligned, like having just visited a chiropractor.

Endosteroidogenesis:

MMD naturally produces steroids within your body.[14] Michael J. Lavery, who has over 25 years of experience in teaching dual-dominance, includes some interesting case studies on this concept of two trained hands. Since I grew up not having this ability, I can describe it today as, "getting there *before you get there*," like a sort of Marvel Comics, Spidey-sense.

This can also translate to having an edge in sports, considering one of baseball's all-time best hitters was also one of the best switch hitters: Mickey Mantle.[9]

Spatial Awareness:

Spatial awareness is an organized understanding of objects in space around us. When viewing Da Vinci's abilities, his spatial awareness is considered the most defining.[10] It is best seen in his art, engineering, sketches, and various handwriting directions, including the mirrored, inverted, and traditional. If you can better understand the bilateral movement of your body, you can better understand your bilateral body's relationship to the space around it.

MMD has caused me to fall more in love with symmetry and alternative spatial expression. This can be seen in my chalk art and photography. I also instinctively started doing lots of normal activities differently once advancing in MMD. For example, when peeling oranges, I now shape them into different forms, such as stars, zig zags, and spirals. When playing the block tower game Jenga, I make symmetric 'X's' all the way up. I also now love walking backwards, fronpacking (aka, front-placed backpacking), ping pong dancing, and handstand\monkey bar inversions, all of which is great for improving posture.

Memory Recollection:

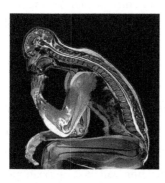

Figure 4.1: Memory recollection increases with MMD

Just as communication is vitally important in our day-to-day lives, our two brain hemispheres have a similar relationship regarding memory development. Memories are encoded in the left hemisphere and retrieved in the right.[5] People with greater communication between the hemispheres, identified by mixed-handedness and ambidexterity, show greater memory recollection.[6] Since MMD increases cross-hemispheric communication, the ability to recall memories increases.[7] Names, alphanumeric patterns, dates, details, etc. become easier to remember with regular MMD practice, a reality that has been known by brain specialists for centuries.[8]

Reaction Time

The habit of choosing your less-dominant side in all activities increases your reaction time. This is because you now have two sets of trained appendages from which to meet a situation. A great example of this is when you unexpectedly need to catch a falling object. The uni-dominant person needs to know how to get their dominant hand positioned just in time to catch the object or risk trying to use their less-dominant hand, if that's the closer one. But the dual-dominant person can react with less effort since they have

endosteroidogenesis in his book, *Whole Brain Power*. The most interesting study is that of Chuck Mellick.[15] At 38 years old, Mellick aspired to be the first baseball pitcher in history to throw 90 MPH with both his right and left hands. While practicing Lavery's MMD routines, Mellick reported seeing and feeling results that caused him to "eat like a horse" just to maintain his body weight. He even went through *a growth spurt*, needing a larger hat, shoe, and ring size! Lavery theorizes that his ambidextrous, golf-ball-bouncing, dual-sledgehammer drills forced Mellick's central and peripheral nervous systems to intensely myelinate axon sheaths.[16] In turn, this accommodates the body with a new level of ability to perform such activity. Lavery's research indicates that this myelination produces unique chemical interactions, leading to the internal, natural synthesis of steroids (aka, endosteroidogenesis).

By this point, Mellick's story was getting picked up by various San Francisco Bay Area reporters, including a CBS affiliate. Before airing the story though, the station discussed this claim of endosteroidogenesis with the local medical community, who responded that it is impossible for a 38-year-old man to be experiencing such changes in his body without taking anabolic steroids. As a result of the controversy, Mellick's story never aired.[17]

Weight Loss:

The average person's brain burns 20% of the body's energy. MMD increases this burn. *Creative Brain Training* author, Diego Irigoyen, who experienced greater attention span, memory recollection, and energy after

Figure 4.3: MMD burns more calories, increasing weight loss

practicing MMD *for just three months,* shares how he and his students were more physically hungry when working to develop dual-dominance.[18] He reports that up to a 40% caloric intake was being consumed through the brain when practicing MMD.[19] This burn manifest itself in at least two areas:

1. **New neural development:** People often describe a "weird, awkward feeling" when practicing MMD, especially in the beginning stages. That challenging, difficult feeling is your brain physically working to create new neural pathways needed to perform your less-dominant, mirrored movements.[20] Creating these pathways requires energy, which comes from food consumption and/or burning energy stored as fat within the body.

2. **Increased muscle development:** The dual-dominant Olympic Handball player, Ebiye Jeremy Udo-Udoma, says that if the average handball player fatigues after 100 throws in a training session, he fatigues after 150. This is because Ebiye can throw 75 times with his dominant hand and 75 times with his less-dominant hand, meaning each arm feel less fatigued, while simultaneously producing more repetitions. As a result, Ebiye can throw for longer periods of time *and* burn more calories.[21]

Personally, I now experience the same sense of extended endurance with longboarding. The ability to push equally with both legs allows me to skate longer than ever before. Considering that 15 years ago I had to stop skateboarding entirely after just 10 years of exclusive, unilateral practice of the sport had completely wrecked my body, I see this ability today as remarkable.[22]

CHAPTER 4
The Benefits of MMD

You may be thinking, "I already have one good hand. Why need another?" Having an extra, equally strong hand on a rainy day sounds like a nice perk, but the benefits of MMD are much greater than just that.

MMD symmetrically grows the brain[1] and aligns the body[2]. This leads to some astonishing benefits, including:

- High-precision balance
- *Neuro-* and *synaptogenesis*
- Heightened spatial awareness
- Improved memory recollection
- Creativity in art and concept development
- Increased athletic, musical, and fine motor skills[3]
- Increased reaction time and hand-eye coordination
- Endosteriodogenesis (natural, internal creation of steroids)
- Prevention/Onset delay of Alzheimer's disease[4]
- *New movement ability*
- Increased longevity
- Weight loss

Creativity in Art and Concept Development:

Dr. Kathryn Ko, a Manhattan-based Neurosurgeon and Fine Artist, believes that her development of ambidexterity while in medical school helped her become a fine artist after already becoming a neurosurgeon. "You need somewhere to focus that extra brain power," says Dr. Ko in relation to the polymathic tendency ambidexters have of adopting a wider spectrum of disciplines.[23]

Figure 4.4: Art and concept development seen in Benjamin Franklin's symmetric design of 13 rings representing the original British American colonies. Printed on colonial U.S. currency

Creative breakthrough is increased by 60% when engaged in the aerobic MMD activity of walking.[24] In fact, Einstein had the idea for his famous $E=MC^2$ equation while performing another aerobic MMD activity: riding his bike.[25]

New Movement Ability:

After years of practicing MMD, I can now do lots of new things, two of which seem trivial:

1) Separating my left pinky toe from the ring toe, and
2) Rolling my tongue counter-clockwise

As someone who could never do these two simple movements growing up, I could not believe the moment I was first able to do them a few years ago. More importantly, it makes me excited to discover new additional things that my MMD-trained body can now perform.[26]

With my improved balance and routine of practicing inversions, I can now do better handstands than ever before. With the ability to now write with either hand, I can do larger chalk drawings than ever before. With the ability to now throw with both hands, I can play wallball for longer, and with more movement variety, than ever before. The same goes for kicking a soccer ball, juggling, ping pong dancing, stretching, and other skills/activities that I learned only within the last few years. And take my word for it: it is exhilarating! The only downside has been finding peers on my same skill level to join in the fun.

Longevity:

Unless you make an equal amount of left and right turns over the lifetime of driving your car, your tires need periodic rotation to maximize their longevity. Of course, you can't rotate your human appendages like rotating car tires, but you can choose to exercise both sides of your bilateral body equally. Does the *machine* of your human body, with its bilateral structure, work optimally for symmetric movement the same as a car? Is functional longevity increased by exercising both sides of your bilateral body equally?

Training one side of your body more than the other leads to imbalances and decreased longevity.[27] This often results in postural problems and various ailments to soft tissue and ligaments that can be avoided with some balancing out.

The mapping of whole body fascial and myofascial linkages, known as *Thomas Myers' Anatomy Trains*, shows that the entire

The ability to imagine and visualize is a powerful tool for achieving goals. In fact, many top athletes talk about the power of visualization as one of their keys to success.[48] Even Albert Einstein said, "Imagination is more important than knowledge."[49]

We will return to more on the science of MMD within the upcoming section on *Mirror Reading*.

that is then put in place of a missing limb from an amputee. With this method, instead of viewing the area of a missing limb, an amputee now *sees a moving limb* – the mirrored image of their intact side. The mirrored image moving fluidly visually convinces their brain

Figure 3.7: Patient using mirror therapy

that the once-missing limb is now whole again.[46]

I tried this technique with my childhood friend, Timmy Gretz, who suffers from left-sided mobility issues caused by a right-sided traumatic brain injury (TBI). Placing a wall mirror between his less-mobile left side and torso, I had Timmy look into the mirror as he worked to raise both arms together. Timmy, who could not see his left arm since it was now being hidden by the mirror, was able to raise his left arm notably higher than before, thanks to help from the mirror!

During mirror box therapy, a portion of Timmy's brain is visually convinced that his disabled left arm is now equal with his capable right arm. As one of our five senses, one would think that sight composes 20% of total sensory recognition, but it is actually closer to 85%.[47] If this 85% can be 100% convinced that what it sees is completely 'normal,' respective mental energy becomes available to help improve sensory mobility.

Figure 3.8: Always excited to hang with my childhood friend, Timmy Gretz

human body is connected.[28] The same can be said for asymmetries. If your right shoulder is stronger than your left, or the left side of your hip is tighter than the right, compensatory patterns will occur.

The two biggest precursors to injury are asymmetries and previous injury.[29] Chronic injuries that inhibit most athletes are, usually, associated with the overuse of one side of the body. When athletes equally use both sides, though, propensity for injury decreases, the body balances out, and longevity increases.[30]

By comparing and contrasting the movements of each side, your body borrows intelligence from the dominant side to educate your less-dominant side. This minimizes movement deficiencies and improves overall athletic capacity, balance, coordination, and strength, leading to longevity.

An online search of workouts associated with longevity

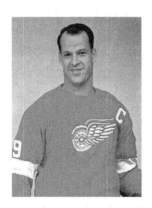

Figure 4.5: NHL legend, Gordie Howe, was the most dual-dominant player and played more seasons than anyone

consistently mentions six activities: walking, swimming, cycling, running, yoga, and tennis.[31] Five of these six activities are symmetric with tennis being the exception, unless you play it MMD-style like former Grand Slam doubles champion, Luke "Dual Hand" Jensen. As the former head tennis coach of Syracuse University, Jensen trained his student athletes to serve ambidextrously, a skill that most players picked up in as little as two months.[32]

Ice hockey legend, Gordie Howe, at 26 seasons through five decades, spent more time in the NHL than anyone, even playing on the same team as his two sons. He was also the best dual-dominant

65

NHL player, using a straight-bladed stick to switch stances between both sides.[33]

65-year-old golfer, Norman White, after surgery to his right shoulder, began focusing more on his less-dominant left side. Today, after years of practice, he plays exclusively switch and recently sunk his first *switch* hole-in-one. His only other hole-in-one happened 15 years earlier, while playing righty. After more than 40 years of playing golf, Norman says his best years are still ahead of him.[34]

Like Norman, it was through seeking physical rehabilitation that I discovered MMD. My 10 years of exclusive, single-sided skateboarding could not be balanced out by repeated chiropractor visits. It was *only* by switching over to my less-dominant side and continuing to skate accordingly that my body was able to realign itself. Not only have I now been skateboarding for more than 25 years – and see no end in sight – but I have gained new abilities, my body feels better than ever, and I'm having more fun!

It is abundantly clear: *the human body is made for MMD.*

immediately told Dara this was the first time that had ever happened. Operating subconsciously from my traditionally 'less-dominant,' side in mirrored direction was exciting. This occurred after more than one year of mirrored reading and writing.

Does this mean that my left-hemisphered Broca's area has now shifted to the right hemisphere? Considering that I am still just as good at writing in the traditional direction with my right hand, my already-developed Broca's area should still be the same, if not better. Perhaps my Broca's area is in the process of duplicating itself onto the right-brain hemisphere and becoming more solidified every time I practice left-handed mirror writing.

Michael J. Lavery reports that his students, after just a few weeks of practicing less-dominant mirrored handwriting, say their dominant hand is working and writing better than ever, and their mirror writing is slowing beginning to look like their dominant writing.[43] In fact, most righties are surprised at how easy it is to write left-handed mirror on a blackboard if their right hand is writing in the traditional direction simultaneously. This can be explained by the fact that the brain hemisphere controlling this movement of the left hand is a mirror-image of the brain hemisphere controlling the right hand.[44]

Mirror Therapy

An MMD exercise worth noting for its scientific intrigue is mirror box therapy.[45] Developed by Dr. V. S. Ramachandran, Neuroscientist and Director of the Center for Brain and Cognition at the University of Southern California, San Diego, mirror box therapy treats amputees suffering from phantom limb pain. The concept is simple: a mirror is positioned inside an open-ended box

- *Neurogenesis, myelination, glucose consumption, and blood flow in both brain hemispheres.* [38]
- *Endosteroidogenesis (the natural, internal creation of bodily steroids), producing pregnenolone, DHEA, testosterone, estradiol, estrogen, and progesterone. This protects the cellular structures in the dentate gyrus, which is where new memory cells are formed inside the hippocampi.* [39]
- *The pre-frontal and frontal lobes to become nourished through sustained beta brainwave activity, creating a cascade of chemical reactions, resulting in the production of adenosine triphosphate (ATP)* [40]

Hemispheric Recognition of Language

The cerebral center for processing language, known as Broca's area, is found in the left-brain hemisphere of nearly 97% of humanity. [41] This makes sense considering most of us, including our ancestors from whom we get our genes, have been using the right hand to write for thousands of years. [42] So, what would have happened if our ancestors chose a more balanced handwriting style, alternating between both hands in mirrored and traditional directions, in line with our symmetric, bilateral design? Would we have two Broca's areas between both hemispheres?

One day in early 2021, I was on the phone with my aunt Dara during a drive from Scranton, Pennsylvania, to Philadelphia. While chatting on my headset, Dara tells me of a new cuisine style she had been experimenting with cooking. It was a cuisine I never heard of before, so I asked her to spell it out. As she did, I instinctively raised my left hand, sounded out the letters, air wrote each letter in mirrored direction, and saw the mirrored word in my mind's eye! I

CHAPTER 5
Mirror Reading

The chosen direction of written languages is arbitrary.[1] Some scripts traditionally go right-to-left, others left-to-right. Some go vertical. Written languages can be character-based, use letters, or whatever else a culture decides makes sense. Like the majority of world scripts, English has held a left-to-right standard – the writing direction best suited for a right hand.[2]

Figure 5.1: "Dream/Magic" cutout mirrored ambigram

Regardless of the directionality a culture chooses for its scripted language, the ability to read and write it is something that no one on Earth is innately born with. Rather, the ability to read and write is

Single-sided body development leads to a smaller corpus callosum.[28] On average, women have a larger corpus callosum than men[29] and process language more evenly between brain hemispheres.[30] The corpus callosum is also 11% larger in most lefties, due to a need of using their less-dominant right hand to operate right hand-designed tools, machines, and objects.[31]

Though there appears to be correlation, science is still not conclusive that right-handed people are left-brain dominant and left-handed people right-brain dominant.[32] Sadly, left-handers are often excluded from neurological research due to the average greater physical difference in their brains, namely that their brains are more symmetric than those of right-handers.[33] When it comes to genetics, some scientists even believe there is a gene for right-handedness, but no gene for left-handedness.[34]

Two great books that discuss the science of MMD using personal case studies from MMD practitioners are *Whole Brain Power*, by Michael J. Lavery, and *Creative Brain Training*, by Diego Irigoyen. Their findings conclude that MMD causes:

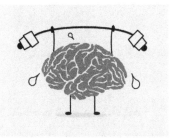

Figure 3.6: MMD is a major workout for your brain

- *Neurons to activate in the opposite temporal lobe, aiding in the development of spatial intelligence* [35]
- *The corpus callosum to thicken and the cerebral cortex, motor strip, and hippocampus to stimulate* [36]
- *Increased skill development by exponentially improving one side of the body, then the other side, and back again* [37]

hemispheres, like all other bilateral muscles, can be equally challenged through the practice of MMD. Neuroscience can now quantify these brain changes with brain scans.[19]

The hands communicate information to the brain as surely as the brain communicates information to the hands,[20] having co-evolved together.[21] As a result, our hands use nearly 25% of the brain's motor strip processing power.[22]

We can develop dual-dominance thanks to our brain's rewiring capabilities, known as neuroplasticity or neurogenesis. Your brain can grow new cells and create new connections as it works to learn mirrored movements.[23] These new brain neurons can be formed at any age.[24]

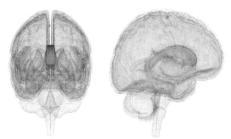

Figure 3.5: Shaded view of the Corpus Callosum at the center of the brain

50% of all brain neurons are located inside the cerebellum, which comprises just 10% of the brain's mass. This cerebellum controls posture, muscle movement, and stores memories for modifying motor function.[25]

When your body is engaged in equal, bilateral exercise, blood flows to both sides of the brain.[26] This blood flow provides oxygen that grows new neurons and synapses within the cerebral cortex, motor strip, and hippocampus. This also thickens your brains' corpus callosum – the fibrous "communication bridge" at the center of your brain and crossing point of all bilateral activity.[27]

learned through practice over time. What happens then to the brain and body when you choose to "flip the script" and work at learning to read and write in mirrored direction?

Mirror reading is an MMD exercise that produces multiple, science-based benefits. We can understand much of this thanks to **Dr. Shelagh Robinson**, Ph.D., a professor of Psychology at Dawson College in Montreal, Canada and Founder of *Mirror Read, Inc.* Her specialized work and research in Visual Perception shows how mirror reading contributes to brain enhancement.

Dr. Robinson started Mirror Read, Inc. in 2010 after spending nearly 20 years practicing mirror writing.[3] Her inspiration came

from Leonardo da Vinci and Lewis Carroll, two of history's most famous mirror writers. Mirror Read, Inc. produces mirror-image books and digital games for kids, read right-to-left, for research, educational, and entertainment purposes.

MirrorRead.com features an iPhone app and web-browser tool that mirror rotates everything on your screen, allowing you to practice mirror reading without needing a physical mirror.

Figure 5.2: Dr. Shelagh Robinson created Mirror Read, Inc. to share the mental benefits of mirror reading

According to Dr. Robinson, mirror reading is a complex cognitive skill studied by researchers across the globe.[4] Scientists use mirror-reversed text to measure spatial rotation skills[5] and test procedural memory in Alzheimer's and Huntington's patients.[6]

Dr. Robinson says the real mysteries of mirror reading lie at the level of the neuron, chemistry, and electrics of learning; *"We are only starting to illuminate the dynamics of neuroplasticity that occur when we read mirrored text."* [7]

MRI brain scan research shows that mirror reading *stimulates gray matter growth* in right-brain cortex regions not associated with traditional reading.[8] Mirror reading is linked to mental rotation, working memory, procedural memory, and spatial transformation.[9] In other words, neurons fire into both brain hemispheres when you practice mirror reading!

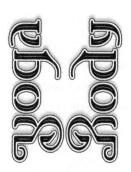

Figure 5.3: "Yoga Body" mirrored vertical ambigram

As you practice reading the mirrored portion of *BIG3MMD,* you will immediately notice that it's harder to read than the traditional direction. Just like your less-dominant hand or foot acclimating over time to general mirrored activity, the less-dominant side of your bilateral brain needs time to acclimate to mirror reading. Like all MMD, mirror reading is a beneficial practice that gets easier over time and brings your body and brain into a more aligned, optimal state.

Tools and Techniques

In addition to the *MirrorRead.com* web browser tool and app, there are a few other tools and methods you can

Figure 5.4: 11 of 26 letters in the English alphabet are identical when viewed mirrored or traditionally

- Clocks are still only read clockwise
- Screws are designed to be more easily tightened by the right hand, using the more powerful supination forearm muscles, as opposed to the weaker pronation muscles [13]
- The vast majority of corkscrews, can openers, microwaves, credit card machines, gas pumps, twist-off bottle caps, watches, spiral notebooks, ladles, measuring cups, desks, scissors, and computer mice are just some of the many items that are designed exclusively for the right hand [14]

Figure 3.4: Children tend to use both hands before adults tell them to focus on just one

As you can see, we have collectively made it difficult to practice many forms of MMD. This has led to producing very few advanced MMD practitioners who can be widely studied.

Third, young children tend to instinctively switch hands between tasks and, periodically, write mirror-style. [15] It seems as if their unadulterated bodies internally know they are designed for MMD. In relation to training his own children to develop ambidexterity, Whole Brain Power author, Michael J. Lavery says, "I feel strongly that there were no negative ramifications from overriding my kids' natural predisposition to favoring one limb over the other." [16]

Your less-dominant hand is connected to a highly functional brain, which can learn many skilled activities, if motivated. [17] The layman's science behind MMD is simple: Moving the right side of your body exercises the left-brain hemisphere, while moving the left side of your body exercises the right-brain hemisphere. [18] The brain

49

being form ambidextrous (aka dual-dominant). It was only until after working hard to make a habit of practicing lifestyle MMD that I realized dual-dominance could even be developed as an adult.

Second, most of us only ever use whatever hand, foot, or stance feels most comfortable. If we only ever do whatever is most comfortable, it would mean rarely practicing disciplines like exercise and healthy eating. We all know the results such a lack of discipline can produce. Developing less-dominant handedness, as connected to brain and body development, is a comparable discipline, but has been practiced much less among cultures for millennia. As a result, this lack of natural, bilateral development has been an unquestionably acceptable norm for most years of humanity on Earth – even though we can each see a bilateral human being designed for symmetric movement staring back at us every time we look in the mirror. This short cutting of our intended development has led to a unilateral design of the human-centric world. As a result, practicing MMD may be difficult to fathom for many of us since there are certain activities and movements we have never performed switch before. For example:

- No car on Earth has its brake pedal on the right and gas pedal on the left [12]
- Most people have never driven a car with the steering wheel on the right side and console features to their left
- There does not yet exist a truly mirrored computer keyboard
- No pair of mass-produced jeans exists with the "fifth pocket," on the left side
- 99.999+% of text you have ever read has been in the traditional direction
- Baseball players never run clockwise around bases

incorporate to practice mirror reading:

- Software programs like **Adobe Acrobat** and **PDF-XChange** allow you to mirror image PDF documents, making it easy to print and read mirrored hard copies.
- **Smart phone editing features** make it possible to horizontally flip photos and screenshots of text into mirrored images.
- Lastly, there's the traditional, **reading-in-a-mirror technique**. To mirror read from my Android phone while going to bed or lying down at a park, I can rest my cell phone on my chest and chin, pointed upwards at a small, hand-held mirror, and read into the mirror. You can also do the same while seated upright using a mirror angled at 45 degrees parallel to the phone.

bilateral brain — an organ designed for mirror processing movement between, both, the left and right mirrored sides of our body.[10]

By this point, I had to remember that this chapter on the science of MMD is being presented backwards; I am not

a unidextrous scientist studying others to see if this all may be true. Rather, I am a dual-dominant, 10-year-practicing, MMD "guinea pig," who is sharing with you the beautiful results I have personally experienced to be true along this journey. Even though I know firsthand that dual-dominance can be developed by the average person and that the benefits are amazing, I want to better understand the science behind why and present the information I have found.

Remember, you can also hear from some of today's foremost MMD practitioners at AmbiLife.org. Like me, they claim that working to develop dual-dominance is one of the greatest choices they have ever made, and advocate the practice for others.

Taking all this into account, it is important to remember three things regarding our approach to understanding the science behind MMD...

First, globally, we are using our unilaterally-developed brains to try understanding how the bilaterally-designed brain works. If our own bilateral brains are not more equally formed through the practice of MMD, are we truly capable of understanding how MMD is supposed to work and be experienced? Before practicing MMD for physical rehabilitation from skateboarding, I never considered ambidexterity as a learnable ability.[11] I had only ever heard of people

anecdotal much of the research has been on dual-dominance, there's room for improvement when understanding the science and nature behind it. Even Dr. Richard Palmer, Professor of Biology at the University of Alberta, admits that the amount we know with confidence about human handedness is so pitiful it's almost shocking.[5]

In developing this chapter, I researched information related to "the science and benefits of developing ambidexterity". Not one article I found said, "Newsflash: Humans are designed for MMD and everyone can benefit from its practice!" Instead, most articles remarked how little we still know about neuroscience,[6] debated the origin – and even definition – of handedness,[7] and drew correlations between handedness and brain lateralization (e.g. language, memory, and other functions residing within different cerebral hemispheres).[8] Some of the articles even claim that developing ambidexterity has negative side effects, leading to ADHD, schizophrenia and other mental disorders.[9]

This may be where MMD and cultural ambidexterity differ. Cultural ambidexterity teaches reading and writing with both hands in one, traditional direction. MMD, on the other hand (quite literally, the other hand), teaches reading and writing with both hands in two directions – mirrored and traditional. While benefit certainly comes from physically exercising both hands in a

Figure 3.2: Symmetric exterior features are designed for equal bilateral mirrored movement

micro-muscular fashion, the practice of using both brain hemispheres to communicate the action of writing in one, unilateral direction may be confusing to spatial recognition portions of our

CONCLUSION

The average human body is mechanically designed for equal bilateral movement (aka MMD), just like a car is mechanically designed for equal left and right turns. Our brain and body receives incredible benefit when engaged in MMD. So, let's treat our bodies according to their natural design by practicing MMD!

Remember, start small and allow your body and brain the time needed to rest, recuperate, and grow from the lifestyle practice of MMD. While young children instinctively practice MMD, it can take adult practitioners years before experiencing fluency. But don't give up! Every adult I know who practices MMD says it is the best choice they have ever made for their mental and physical well-being. MMD produces many benefits, including body realignment, high-precision balance, brain efficiency, weight-loss, increased memory, heightened spatial awareness, physical longevity, and more.

So, what do you think? Is MMD worth spending the time and effort to practice for achieving physical rehabilitation goals, peak performance, and an optimal, creative neurological state?

We read of famous luminaries, polymaths, and naturephiles who historically practiced a spectrum of MMD. Do you believe MMD was responsible for making distinctive brain changes that helped create their uniqueness? Do these MMD-related qualities intrigue you?

In writing *BIG3MMD*, my goal has been greater than just presenting to you information on the history and science of MMD; I want to inspire you to adopt the MMD lifestyle and experience the benefits for yourself!

MMD may be the greatest missing piece of basic human development and primary education in our world. Imagine the state of this planet if we all developed our brains and bodies according to their design for equal bilateral movement. We would become collectively greater than all the polymaths, luminaries, and naturephiles listed in this book. What a great world that would be!

So, are you ready to practice MMD? You can start today! Ambidexters are self-taught by the greatest teacher: their own bilateral sides, focusing first on less-dominant mirrored movement. No additional coach is needed to begin and continue MMD, although insight can always be gained from masters of the practice. Visit *AmbiLife.org* for more information on MMD, to get tips from advanced practitioners, and to join the MMD community.

CHAPTER 3
The Science of MMD

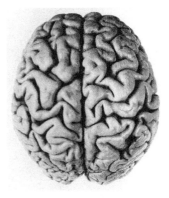

Figure 3.1: Like our asymmetrically-placed internal organs, the brain performs different functions within the bilateral hemispheres. As far as body movement goes, though, the brain is designed for achieving symmetric performance

The most powerful organ in your body is also the most intelligent 'machine' of all time – our human brain.[1] At just 3 pounds in the average adult, the human brain comprises only 2% of total body weight,[2] but consumes a whopping 20% of the body's energy supply.[3] The historic individuals featured in BIG3MMD possessed brains that could be considered efficient and well-developed. But how much of this reality has to do with their practice of MMD? What exactly does MMD do to the brain?

Although some estimates say only 1% of the global population is dual-dominant,[4] how many people do you know intentionally work to develop both sides of their body in all activities? I bet it's currently still far less than 1%. And of those people, how many have been extensively researched? Considering how piecemeal and

ACKNOWLEDGMENTS

Thanks to...

My childhood friend, **Timmy Gretz**, for inadvertently teaching me more about the human brain than anyone. I am always sorry about your accident, but it has shown me just how important that squishy, 3-pound organ/machine inside our head really is and what it is more capable of accomplishing through MMD.

My fellow 'right-handed,' lefty-learning ambidexters: **Ebiye Jeremy, Dr. Kathryn Ko, Diego Irigoyen,** and **Michael J. Lavery.** Your stories have inspired me to share my own. And just like all of you, I am excited to see lots of people join our *ambitribe* and benefit greatly from practicing MMD.

My left-handed Editor and Aunt, **Patricia Wallace**, for her hard work in making the most sense of my writing. Incidentally, she was a natural mirror writer as a young child.

My *gringo amigo*, **David Reisman**, and fellow *Seton Catholic High School Alumni*, **Maria Recupero English** and **Richard Mogavero**, for insight and editorial assistance.

My *frienemy*, **Adam Jones**, for kicking my butt into making this book cover better than the "rave card" it was originally going to look like.

73

My personal coach, **Daniel Vázquez Montaño**, for all the advice, tools, and encouragement to work hard and push through to make this book a reality.

My friends and neighbors, **Simón Gutkin, Cat Valverde, Brad Morris, Miguel Rodriguez, Kenny Donohue, Katie Butler, Seth Goldenberg,** and **Sebastian Reyes,** for giving me great additional content and for receiving my many months of mental/verbal processing while putting this book together.

Dave Srebro and the *Northeastern PA Council* of the **Boy Scouts of America** for all the great years of left-handed handshakes, square knot-tying, and lessons learned about Baden-Powell.

Dr. Shelagh Robinson for her work in bringing mirror reading to the masses through her research and creation of *MirrorRead.com.*

Dr. V.S. Ramachandran for his work in developing mirror therapy and for what it has done to help my friend, Timmy Gretz.

Philadelphia's **Parkway Central Library** and the **University of Pennsylvania's Van Pelt-Dietrich Library** for accommodating me over the many hours I spent there researching and writing for this book.

everything on our screens. This way, we can all practice mirror reading and become more brilliant like Leonardo. Thanks, Bill!

In summary, there is nothing within the mechanical design of our human body that limits it to writing – or performing any other lateral activity – with just one hand. The only way to become proficient at mirrored movement is through practice. As a 10-year MMD practitioner who has experienced subsequent body realignment and increased brain efficiency, it is clear to me that Leonardo da Vinci filled the 7,200+ pages of his personal notebooks with mirrored and inverted handwriting for three reasons:[63]

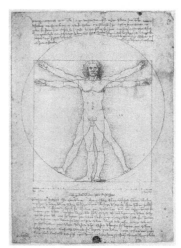

Figure 2.18: Symmetry, beauty, and mirrored writing in Da Vinci's sketch of the Vitruvian Man

1. To symmetrically exercise his brain and body,
2. Increase spatial awareness, and
3. Honor his organic-mechanical design for equal, bilateral movement.

As a sidenote, one of Da Vinci's notebooks – the 72-page Codex Leicester – is the most expensive book in the world. It was bought at auction for $30 million dollars by Bill Gates, who has toured it around the world to educate people on the insights and achievements of Da Vinci...[64]

Mr. Gates, if you're reading this (I know you read a lot of books), please make a feature on Microsoft products that mirror images

ABOUT THE AUTHOR

Chalking it up at 13th & Chestnut in Downtown Philly

Jim Houliston is a Philadelphia-based, dual-dominant artist, athlete, educator, and author of the world's first modern biscriptal book – *BIG3MMD: History's Ambidextrous and the Benefits of Mirror Movement Development*. He grew up in Old Forge, Pennsylvania, received his B.A. in Communication Studies from West Chester University of PA, and spent 14 years living between San Diego, California and Tijuana and Guadalajara, Mexico...*Órale!*

His next work is to facilitate a community of MMD practitioners, create and promote MMD products, and publish another biscriptal book – one about *today's* ambidextrous. Learn more at *AmbiLife.org*.

Jim's additional interests include:

- Seeing the U.S. end the *War on Drugs,* invest more money in drug abuse prevention, education, and rehabilitation, and help turn Latin America into the secure and thriving region it deserves to be.
- Seeing people suffering from Church-related Anxiety Disorder (C-RAD) have adequate and honest community within the contemporary church scene.
- Sharing his thoughts on fixing the world's problems and what the "end times" may look like.

A fun day for Jim includes long-distance longboarding, rail walking, ambiball, inversions, chalk art, ping pong dancing, skate yoga, backwards walking, and enjoying craft beer with friends.

Vinci's considering the exhaustive detail in which he wrote about light, shadow, human form, water, air, botany, mechanics, and more. He even considered the job of a painter as to "imitate all the works of Nature which adorn the world."[60]

While Da Vinci was certainly curious, intelligent, disciplined, and talented, it is arguably his uncommon sense of spatial awareness that best defines him. How much of this ability, though, was he born with? How much of it did he actually work to develop? I am not alone in believing that Leonardo's choice to develop traditional, mirrored, and inverted handwriting is

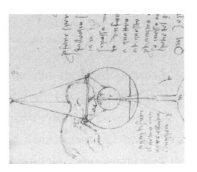

Figure 2.17: Da Vinci's discovery of the eyeball as a camera obscura

what shaped much of his mind to observe and articulate the world as he did.

Diego Irigoyen, one of the best mirror and inverted writers I know today, shares in his book, *Creative Brain Training: Increase Attention Span, Build Confidence, and Stimulate Creativity*, the belief that much of Leonardo's genius was nurtured through his practice of mirror writing.[61] Da Vinci even considered mirrors as the master of painters, saying, "the mind of the painter must resemble a mirror," and that "the mirror is our teacher, giving us a fresh eye".[62]

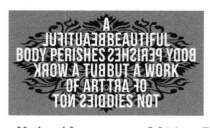

Figure 2.16: Symmetry – one of three chief forms of beauty, according to the Da Vinci-inspiring Aristotle

actually improves when you focus simply on developing your less-dominant side, a concept mentioned earlier as manual transfer learning.[54] As a highly skilled embodiment of both art and science, Da Vinci is synonymous with the word 'polymath,' or one who is learned in many subjects. His personal notebooks highlight a mind working in otherworldly overdrive, capable of computing more on various topics than the average brain. 19th-century transcribers of Da Vinci's writings even commented that many of his entries can only be understood by specialists of corresponding disciplines, whether Physics, Mechanics, Biology, etc.[55] Interestingly, like Benjamin Franklin, Da Vinci lacked years of formal education.[56]

Da Vinci's practice of dual-directional handwriting not only equally balances the micro muscles of the hands and bilateral posture of the body, but also fosters brain growth.[57] If it's true that MMD grows the brain and its capacity for computative, observational power, then Leonardo manifests the heights of practice.

In addition to mirrored direction, why did Da Vinci invert his handwriting? When addressing this, it's important to note that Leonardo was the first person to understand that the human eye performs as a camera obscura – inverting an image within the back of the eye before the brain reverts it again.[58] This discovery may have compelled Leonardo to invert his writing as an exercise for increasing spatial awareness and better understanding our connection within the natural order.[59] Observing nature was an obvious passion of Da

REFERENCES

How to Read a Biscriptal Book

1 – Emma G. Duerden and Daniele Laverdure-Dupont. *JneuroSci.org,* "Practice Makes Cortex," August 27, 2008. https://www.jneurosci.org/content/jneuro/28/35/8655.full.pdf

2 – Michael C. Corballis. *Frontiers in Human Neuroscience,* "Mirror-Image Equivalence and Interhemispheric Mirror-Image Reversal," April 2018. https://www.researchgate.net/publication/287968292_Interhemispheri c_mirror-image_reversal

Disclaimer

1 – David Wolman. *A Left-Hand Turn Around the World: Chasing the Mystery and Meaning of All Things Southpaw* (De Capo Press, 2005), pages 14-15

2 – Chris McManus. *Right Hand, Left Hand: The Origins of Asymmetry in Brains, Bodies, Atoms and Cultures* (Orion Publishing, 2003), pages 329-330

Introduction

1 – Jim Houliston. *AmbiLife.org,* "Today's MMD Practitioners," September 17, 2021. https://ambilife.org/todays-mmd-practitioners/

2 – *Vocabulary.com*, Definition 'Ambidextrous'
https://www.vocabulary.com/dictionary/ambidextrous
3 – David Wolman. *A Left-Hand Turn Around the World: Chasing the Mystery and Meaning of All Things Southpaw* (De Capo Press, 2005), page 15

4 – Jim Houliston. *AmbiLife.org*, "Benefits of MMD," September 24, 2021. https://ambilife.org/benefits-of-mmd/

5 – *History.com*, "Leonardo da Vinci," December 2, 2009. https://www.history.com/topics/renaissance/leonardo-da-vinci

6 – Leonardo da Vinci, translated by Jean Paul Richter (1888). *The Complete Notebooks of Leonardo da Vinci* (Eternal Sun Books, 2016), page 22

7 – Adam Sinicki. *TheBioneer.com*, "Training Ambidexterity – For Athleticism, Creativity, and Symmetry," March 26, 2021. https://www.thebioneer.com/ambidexterity-training/
***The term "*Manual transfer learning*" is taken from a book I read over two years ago that discusses this same cited concept as "*Intermanual Transfer of Skill.*" Frankly, I have not been able to relocate "*manual transfer learning*" when reviewing the books I have read, but still prefer this term, so I choose to use it throughout *BIG3MMD*. I hope to relocate this reference one day and include it in an updated version of *BIG3MMD*.

Chapter 1: History's Spectrum of MMD

1 – Mario Livio. *HuffPost.com*, "Why Are We Symmetrical?," December 6, 2017. https://www.huffpost.com/entry/why-are-we-symmetrical_b_1836534

2 – David Wolman. *A Left-Hand Turn Around the World: Chasing the Mystery and Meaning of All Things Southpaw* (De Capo Press, 2005), page 46

became obsessed with analyzing the bilateral symmetry that allows birds to fly.[45] Even the earliest drafts of how to build a flying conveyance for humans came from Da Vinci.[46]

Leonardo's love of symmetry may have been partly inspired by Aristotle, the Greek polymath and student of Plato.[47] Aristotle wrote that symmetry, order, and definiteness, were the three chief forms of beauty, proven by science everywhere.[48] It is also believed that Aristotle's observations on underwater acoustics, meteorology, and color perspective inspired Da Vinci.[49]

Considering Leonardo's mirrored handwriting style, some claim he was simply left-handed or dyslexic,[50] even though he penned right-handed traditional whenever writing to someone else.[51] This ability for Da Vinci to equally use both hands can be explained by the fact that less-dominant mirrored handwriting can be developed by any average person, at any age.[52] Remember, humans do not enter the world with an innate ability to read or write, let alone with a 'dominant' hand. Rather, we spend years working to develop it. The same is true for an average adult developing less-dominant mirror writing or mirror reading – with a lot of practice, it can become as natural as the traditional direction.

Thankfully, for the average adult, developing your less-dominant side in mirrored motion takes less time than the initial development of your dominant side. This is because your dominant side works as a seasoned teacher to streamline the process for your less-dominant side when learning the same activity mirrored.[53] One great benefit from this process is that your more-dominant side

39

among his peers to exhibit dual-dominance. Michelangelo, Raphael, and Dante were also Italian Renaissance creatives known to be ambidextrous.[41]

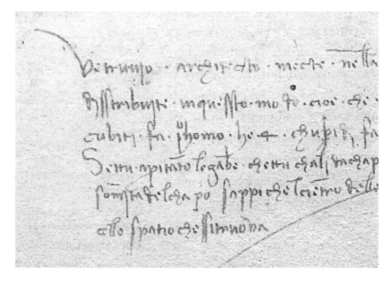

Figure 2.14: Mirrored writing from one of Da Vinci's 7,200+ personal notebook pages

Da Vinci was a keen and curious observer. Based on his meticulous, anatomical drawings of human exterior features, skeletons, muscles, joints, and ligaments – observed while secretly dissecting human cadavers[42] – Da Vinci would have noticed the body's design for symmetric, bilateral movement.[43] As an engineer, he may have noted this symmetry and concluded that no Creator of such an organic machine would ever intend for it to move and develop asymmetrically. Thus, Da Vinci would have found it appropriate to adopt the combined practice of mirrored and traditional handwriting, a practice that symmetrically develops the body. In fact, many of his more inventive sketches are full of symmetry, like his Rhombicuboctahedron and Vitruvian Man.[44] He

3 – *IfitTraining.co.uk,* "Asymmetry in the Human Body," January 13, 2017. https://www.ifittraining.co.uk/insights/asymmetry-human-body/

4 – Diego Irigoyen. *Lettering-Daily.com,* "How to Become Ambidextrous in 6 Easy Steps," 2018. https://www.lettering-daily.com/6-steps-to-become-ambidextrous/

5 – *TheOTtoolbox.com,* "Writing with Both Hands – What you Need to Know," April 15, 2019. https://www.theottoolbox.com/writing-with-both-hands-what-you-need/

6 – Jean-Paul Fischer. *TheConversation.com,* "Understanding children's mirror writing," November 29, 2017. https://theconversation.com/understanding-childrens-mirror-writing-87948

7 - *WorldHistoryEdu.com,* "5 Great Accomplishments of Ancient Greece," February 27, 2021. https://www.worldhistoryedu.com/great-achievements-of-ancient-greece/

8 – *Wikipedia.org,* "Ancient Greek," February 13, 2022. https://wikipedia.org/wiki/Ancient_Greek

9 – *Wikipedia.org,* "Boustrophedon," February 18, 2022. https://wikipedia.org/wiki/Boustrophedon

10 – Igor Chykalov. *Medium.com,* "Brain and Body Ambidexterity," August 26, 2020. https://medium.com/illumination/brain-and-body-ambidexterity-e6d92ad3cd19

11 – John Jackson. *Ambidexterity: Or Two-Handedness and Two-Brainedness, An Argument For Natural Development And Rational Education.* (Dryden House London, 1905), pages 143-144

12 – *Wikipedia.org,* "Rongorongo," February 9, 2022. https://wikipedia.org/wiki/Rongorongo

13 – *Warehouse-13-Artifact-Database-Wiki.com,* "Leonardo da Vinci's Notebook," https://warehouse-13-artifact-database.fandom.com/wiki/Leonardo_da_Vinci%27s_Notebook

14 – *Wikiwand.com,* "Mirror writing," February 18, 2022. https://www.wikiwand.com/en/Mirror_writing

15 – John Jackson. *Ambidexterity: Or Two-Handedness and Two-Brainedness, An Argument For Natural Development And Rational Education.* (Dryden House London, 1905), pages 114 & 145

16 – Ibid., pages 114, 117, 135, 154, 157

17 – Ibid., page 128

18 – Ibid., page 114

19 – *Wikipedia.org,* "Switch pitcher," November 28, 2021. https://wikipedia.org/wiki/Switch_pitcher

20 – Chris McManus. *Right Hand, Left Hand: The Origins of Asymmetry in Brains, Bodies, Atoms and Cultures* (Orion Publishing, 2003), page 364

21 – *Wikipedia.org,* "Plato," February 20, 2022. https://wikipedia.org/wiki/Plato

22 – Luke Mastin. *RightLeftRightWrong.com,* "History of Handedness – Ancient History," 2012. https://www.rightleftrightwrong.com/history_ancient.html

23 – Chris McManus. *Right Hand, Left Hand: The Origins of Asymmetry in Brains, Bodies, Atoms and Cultures* (Orion Publishing, 2003), page McManus, page 364

24 – Ibid., page 282

25 – Ibid., pages 282-283

26 – Lisa Marder. *ThoughtCo.com,* "10 Famous Left-Handed Artists: Chance or Destiny?" August 27, 2018. https://www.thoughtco.com/a-list-of-left-handed-artists-4077979

27 – Andreas Barth. *MusicExperience.co.za,* "10 Most Famous Left-Handed Musicians," September 17, 2016. https://www.musicexperience.co.za/blogs/news/64316227-10-most-famous-left-handed-musicians

28 – Christopher Bergland. *PsychologyToday.com,* "Einstein's Genius Linked to Well-Connected Brain Hemispheres," October 5, 2013. https://www.psychologytoday.com/us/blog/the-athletes-way/201310/einsteins-genius-linked-well-connected-brain-hemispheres

Leonardo da Vinci

Among polymaths, luminaries, and naturephiles, it's easy to see Leonardo da Vinci as all three. He was an artist, engineer, scientist, theorist, sculptor, and architecture. His personal notebooks are full of insight into anatomy, astronomy, optics, botany, cartography, hydrodynamics, painting, and paleontology.[37]

For some, mystery still surrounds the personal, secretive 'handwriting' style of this Italian Renaissance genius. Just like the ancient Greeks with boustrophedon and the Easter Islanders with rongorongo, Leonardo wrote in both mirrored and inverted script.[38]

Experts from the Opificio delle Pietre Dure, a research and art

Figure 2.13: History's quintessential dual-dominant polymath: Leonardo da Vinci

conservation institute in Florence, Italy, discovered that Leonardo wrote right-handed traditional and left-handed mirrored in his landscape drawing at just 21 years-old.[39] What exactly inspired the young man to work at equally developing both sides of his body via mirrored handwriting? One belief is that Da Vinci switched hands for physical rehabilitation purposes. In one journal entry, Da Vinci thanks God for "having escaped from murderers with only one hand dislocated."[40] Or was Da Vinci inspired by a mentor, teacher, or contemporaries to practice MMD? After all, Leonardo wasn't alone

feasible. Considering though that he still lived another 11 years after penning his Petition, it would seem odd if Franklin never actually worked during this time to develop both hands, a practice he mentions being so important within the Petition essay.

Figure 2.12: Franklin extending his left hand to George Washington in "The Bond," sculpture by Jim West in downtown Philadelphia, Pennsylvania

Whether Franklin passionately practiced MMD is questionable. However, note that Franklin, like Da Vinci and Baden-Powell, exhibited our three hallmarks of a prolific ambidexter:

1. Polymath
2. Luminary who catalyzed human advancements [34]
3. Naturephile who keenly observed the created order, as seen in his love for swimming,[35] charting of the Gulf stream, first proposal of Daylight Savings Time,[36] and applications of electricity[37]

Considering the evidence, one can conclude that Benjamin Franklin practiced a developmental form of MMD during his lifetime.

29 – *NPS.gov*, "Thomas Jefferson," February 11, 2022. https://www.nps.gov/jeff/learn/historyculture/thomas-jefferson.htm

30 – Cristin O'Keefe Aptowicz. *SmithsonianMag.com*, "Before Dr. Mutter, Surgery Was a Dangerous and Horrifically Painful Ordeal," September 4, 2014. https://www.smithsonianmag.com/history/dr-mutter-surgery-was-dangerous-and-horrifically-painful-ordeal-180952580/

31 – Matt Blitz. *SmithsonianMag.com*, "How Einstein's Brain Ended Up at the Mütter Museum in Philadelphia," April 17, 2015. https://www.smithsonianmag.com/travel/how-einsteins-brain-ended-mutter-museum-philadelphia-180954987/

32 – Chris McManus. *Right Hand, Left Hand: The Origins of Asymmetry in Brains, Bodies, Atoms and Cultures* (Orion Publishing, 2003), page 179

33 – Robert Stacey. *ArtMuseum.Utoronto.ca*, "Sir Daniel Wilson (1816–1892): Ambidextrous Polymath," September, 2001. https://artmuseum.utoronto.ca/exhibition/sir-daniel-wilson/

34 – John Jackson. *Ambidexterity: Or Two-Handedness and Two-Brainedness, An Argument For Natural Development And Rational Education.* (Dryden House London, 1905), page 148

35 – Janice Arkatov. *LAtimes.com*, "'Carroll' Through the Looking Glass," January 22, 1989. https://www.latimes.com/archives/la-xpm-1989-01-22-ca-1100-story.html

36 – Zeena Nackerdien. *WordGuru.rocks*, "Through the Looking Glass with Da Vinci and Carroll," 2018. https://www.wordguru.rocks/single-post/2018/07/11/through-the-looking-glass-with-da-vinci-and-carroll

37 – *Wikipedia.org*, "Ambigram," February 18, 2022. https://wikipedia.org/wiki/Ambigram

38 – Mohammed Noor. *WhatsUpLife.in*, "Bet you didn't know these 10 Famous people were Ambidextrous," May 31, 2017. https://www.whatsuplife.in/list-famous-ambidextrous-celebs-people-celebrities

39 – Sarah Pruitt. *History.com*, "The First Left-handed President Was Ambidextrous and Multilingual," September 1, 2018. https://www.history.com/news/first-left-handed-president-ambidextrous-multilingual

40 – Lutesha Sadhewa. *RightBrainedLeftHanded.blogspot.com*, "Ambidextrous," August 8, 2009. http://rightbrainedlefthanded.blogspot.com/2009/08/ambidextrous.html

41 – Eddie Deezen. *NeatOrama.com*, "12 Things You May Not Know About Houdini," October 29, 2014. https://www.neatorama.com/2014/10/29/12-Things-You-May-Not-Know-About-Houdini/

42 – *BuzzWorthy.com*, "6 Facts You Didn't Know About Illusionist Harry Houdini," 2018. https://www.buzzworthy.com/six-facts-you-didnt-know-about-illusionist-harry-houdini/

43 – Arthur Moses. *WildAboutHoudini.com*, "Houdini claimed he was building a "health house"," February 9, 2019. https://www.wildabouthoudini.com/2019/02/houdinis-claim-that-he-was-building.html

44 – Chris McManus. *Right Hand, Left Hand: The Origins of Asymmetry in Brains, Bodies, Atoms and Cultures* (Orion Publishing, 2003), page 356

45 – David Gracey. *SuperMindHacker.com*, "Was Albert Einstein Left Or Right Brained? The Shocking Answer!" 2020. https://www.supermindhacker.com/was-albert-einstein-left-or-right-brained/

46 - Christopher Bergland. *PsychologyToday.com*, "Einstein's Genius Linked to Well-Connected Brain Hemispheres," October 5, 2013. https://www.psychologytoday.com/us/blog/the-athletes-way/201310/einsteins-genius-linked-well-connected-brain-hemispheres

47 – Mithu Storoni. *Inc.com*, "The Scientist Who Studied Einstein's Brain Learned That These 5 Factors Make You Smarter," August 3, 2017. https://www.inc.com/mithu-storoni/what-einsteins-brain-tells-us-about-intelligence-a.html

telling him, "Bummer on your wrist, Thomas, but it's no big deal. Both sides are made for EQUAL use, so just keep developing your left hand!"

In further connecting Franklin and Jefferson, author Walter Isaacson referred to them both as "Avatars of the Enlightenment."[31] Jefferson also proceeded Franklin as the second U.S. Ambassador to France.

Figure 2.11: Franklin made many inventions, including Bifocals for better reading

Let us also return for a moment to Franklin's unfinished autobiography, which he wrote between 1771 and 1790, the year he died. It is a work that recalls his life from birth up until 1757, meaning there is still another 22 unaccounted years before he writes his Petition essay in 1779.[32] Perhaps it is within this time period that Franklin dove into a practice of MMD. Or perhaps he practiced MMD to some degree beforehand, but never felt it necessary to mention such details within the busy accounts of political, scientific, economic, philosophical, and civic thoughts he expressed within his autobiography. Or again, perhaps he never practiced MMD at all, outside of mirror reading while setting mirrored type for printing.

Interestingly, Franklin's autobiographical writings arrived at the printer penned in his own, nearly-illegible handwriting.[33] Subsequently, the French publishers, who were the first to print his autobiography, faced extended delays as they struggled to read his awkward scribble. Was this atrocious penmanship due to Franklin working to develop his less-dominant hand or was it just the case of an older man overusing his more-dominant hand? Either sounds

Dr. Joyce Chaplin, Professor of Early American History at Harvard University, notes that Franklin was "clever with his hands," good at thinking, and hyper-literate," to be able to arrange inverted, mirrored type settings and mirror read them for accuracy."[27] One can conclude that Franklin, who only received two years of elementary education, practiced thousands of hours of mirror reading before retiring from printing at age 42. Soon after, Franklin would make up for his "lack of education," by receiving five honorary degrees, including doctorates from Harvard, Yale, and Oxford universities.[28] Even considering the vast array of things Franklin did and became known for, he still acutely identified with this mirror-reading profession – so much so that he referred to himself in his own will later in life simply as "Benjamin Franklin, Printer."

Many left-handers feel more natural writing mirrored direction (aka right-to-left), such as the Beatles' Sir Paul McCartney did as a young child.[29] Did Benjamin Franklin have a left-handed eye for mirror script that gave him a more natural ability to set type faster than competitors? His Petition of the Left Hand points out that dual-dominance has excellent benefits. And what does dual-dominance require? A lot of mirror movement!

Let us recall from Chapter 1 how Benjamin Franklin's contemporary, Thomas Jefferson, broke his right wrist in France. Franklin wrote his Petition while in France, less than five years before Jefferson arrived.[30] Jefferson and Franklin were together in France for one year before parting ways. Even though Franklin was already back in America when Jefferson broke his wrist, Jefferson may have had knowledge of the Petition, inspiring him to further develop his southpaw side more than just did his need of physical rehabilitation. When the two reunited in Philadelphia four years later, in early 1790, I can imagine Franklin sharing with Jefferson his Petition,

48 – David Wolman. *A Left-Hand Turn Around the World: Chasing the Mystery and Meaning of All Things Southpaw* (De Capo Press, 2005), page 202

49 – *Wikipedia.org,* "Albert Einstein's brain," February 17, 2022. https://wikipedia.org/wiki/Albert_Einstein%27s_brain

50 – *TheGoan.net,* "Think right for those who are left(ies)," October 12, 2019. https://www.thegoan.net//think-right-for-those-who-are-left(ies)/54737.html

51 – Erik Kersten. *EscherInHetPaleis.nl,* "Left-handedness," August 13, 2019. https://www.escherinhetpaleis.nl/escher-today/left-handedness/?lang=en

52 – Sean Michaels. *TheGuardian.com,* "Was Jimi Hendrix's ambidexterity the key to his virtuosity?" February 10, 2010. https://www.theguardian.com/music/2010/feb/25/jimi-hendrix-ambidexterity-virtuosity

53 - Andreas Barth. *MusicExperience.co.za,* "10 Most Famous Left-Handed Musicians," September 17, 2016. https://www.musicexperience.co.za/blogs/news/64316227-10-most-famous-left-handed-musicians

Chapter 2: The Big Three – Da Vinci, Franklin, and Baden-Powell

BADEN-POWELL

1 – *Wikipedia.org,* "Robert Baden-Powell, 1st Baron Baden-Powell," February 20, 2022. https://wikipedia.org/wiki/Robert_Baden-Powell,_1st_Baron_Baden-Powell

2 – *OA-BSA.org,* "Lord Baden-Powell," https://oa-bsa.org/history/lord-baden-powell

3 – *Scout.org,* "Meet Baden-Powell," https://www.scout.org/bp

4 – *AtlasObscura.com,* "The Founder of the Boy Scouts Hid Maps in Insect Drawings," June 20, 2016.

https://www.atlasobscura.com/articles/the-founder-of-the-boy-scouts-hid-maps-in-insect-drawings

5 – *Wikipedia.org*, "Scouting for Boys," January 9, 2022.
https://wikipedia.org/wiki/Scouting_for_Boys

6 – Jim Houliston. *YouTube.com*, "The Ambidexterity of Lord Robert Baden-Powell – Boy Scouts' Founders," September 21, 2021.
https://www.youtube.com/watch?v=eJUPHZUJlX4

7 – Prerita Chawla. *Medium.com*, "Should Students be Trained to be Ambidextrous?" August 6, 2020. https://medium.com/indian-thoughts/should-students-be-trained-to-be-ambidextrous-6056bc07ba2d

8 – *Wikipedia.org*, "Polymath," January 28, 2022.
https://wikipedia.org/wiki/Polymath

9 – Steve Henning. *Scouters.us*, "Merit Badges, Past and Present, And Their Evolution," February 14, 2018.
http://www.scouters.us/Merit.php

10 – Michael J. Lavery. *Whole Brain Power: The Fountain of Youth for the Mind and Body* (Lulu Press, 2008), page 143

11 – Melanie Radzicki McManus. *HowStuffWorks.com*, "How to Tie the Impossible Knot," June 18, 2015.
https://adventure.howstuffworks.com/survival/wilderness/how-to-tie-the-impossible-knot.htm

12 – Charlie Wood. *BrainFacts.org*, "Does Using Your Non-Dominant Hand Make You Smarter?" August 9, 2019.
https://www.sfn.org/sitecore/content/Home/BrainFacts2/Thinking-Sensing-and-Behaving/Thinking-and-Awareness/2019/Does-Using-Your-Non-Dominant-Hand-Make-You-Smarter-080919

13 – The Brisbane Courier. *Trove.nla.gov.au*, "Lord Baden-Powell's Ambidexterity," June 2, 1931.
https://trove.nla.gov.au/newspaper/article/21716049

BENJAMIN FRANKLIN

So, was Franklin right-handed, left-handed, mix-handed, or dual-dominant? This essay, written in the voice of the abused and underdeveloped left hand, laments a general, cultural neglect of the southpaw side; an odd grievance to be made by any exclusive right-hander. And, while a 1762 painting shows Franklin holding a quill in his right hand,[21] some sources say he was left-handed,[22] including that he signed both the Declaration of Independence and the U.S. Constitution left-handed.[23] He is also portrayed in the movie 1776 as a lefty. So, was he dual-dominant? Professor of Medical Education and Psychology, Chris McManus, a handedness expert and author of *Right Hand, Left Hand: the Origins of Asymmetry in Brains, Bodies, Atoms, and Cultures*, says the Petition essay suggests Franklin either held a belief in dual-dominance or was just playing a literary joke.[24]

Figure 2.10: "Fish and Visitors stink after three days." Since the age of 12, Franklin set and read mirrored print type just like this.

There is another sign, though, that Franklin practiced MMD. He was a printing apprentice to his oldest brother, James, who started the second newspaper in America, *The New-England Courant*. Since the age of 12, Franklin's job was to prepare the printing by setting type.[25] All of these metallic type settings were mirror-imaged so as to be viewed in the traditional direction once printed on paper.[26]

subsistence fall upon my sister and myself. If any indisposition should attack my sister—and I mention it in confidence upon this occasion, that she is subject to the gout, the rheumatism, and cramp, without making mention of other accidents—what would be the fate of our poor family? Must not the regret of our parents be excessive, at having placed so great a difference between sisters who are so perfectly equal? Alas! we must perish from distress; for it would not be in my power even to scrawl a suppliant petition for relief, having been obliged to employ the hand of another in transcribing the request which I have now the honor to prefer to you.

Condescend, sirs, to make my parents sensible of the injustice of an exclusive tenderness, and of the necessity of distributing their care and affection among all their children equally.

I am, with a profound respect, Sirs, your most obedient servant,

The Left Hand

The essay's main themes:

- Addressed to educators the same year Franklin's school becomes America's first university
- Classified both left and right hands as natural equals in need of equal development
- Listed detrimental\wasteful results from forcing a child to use primarily one hand
- Cited using both hands as necessary to survival in case of accident

14 – *Wikipedia.org,* "Benjamin Franklin," February 21, 2022. https://wikipedia.org/wiki/Benjamin_Franklin

15 – *Wikipedia.org,* "The Autobiography of Benjamin Franklin," January 31, 2022. https://wikipedia.org/wiki/The_Autobiography_of_Benjamin_Franklin

16 – *MSN.com,* "Athletes and A-listers who are ambidextrous," December 10, 2021. https://www.msn.com/en-us/travel/news/athletes-and-a-listers-who-are-ambidextrous/ss-AARET0t#image=10

17 – Benjamin Franklin. *LeftHandersLegacy.org,* "A Petition of the Left Hand," 1779. https://lefthanderslegacy.org/left-handed-profiles/a-petition-of-the-left-hand-by-benjamin-franklin/

18 – J.V. Crum III. *ConsciousMillionaire.com,* "Become the 1st Millionaire in Your Family," 2014. https://consciousmillionaire.com/PDF/1ST-MILLIONAIRE.pdf

19 – Barry Popik. *BarryPopik.com,* "An investment in knowledge always pays the best interest," November 4, 2014. https://www.barrypopik.com/index.php/new_york_city/entry/an_investment_in_knowledge

20 – *Upenn.edu,* "Penn's History," https://www.upenn.edu/about/history

21 – J.L. Bell. *Boston1775.blogspot.com,* "Benjamin Franklin: Lefty or Righty?" May 7, 2009. https://boston1775.blogspot.com/2009/05/benjamin-franklin-lefty-or-righty.html

22 – *LeftHandersLegacy.org,* "Benjamin Franklin," 2018. https://lefthanderslegacy.org/benjamin-franklin/

23 – Melvin D. Saunders. *Mind-Course.com,* "Let Us Introduce You To Our New Ambidexterity Exercise," 2013. http://www.mind-course.com/ambi.html

24 – Chris McManus. *Right Hand, Left Hand: The Origins of Asymmetry in Brains, Bodies, Atoms and Cultures* (Orion Publishing, 2003), page 330

25 – *Benjamin-Franklin-History.org*, "Benjamin Franklin, the Printer," http://www.benjamin-franklin-history.org/benjamin-franklin-printer/

26 – *SlaveryAndRemembrance.org*, "Printer and Binder," https://www.slaveryandremembrance.org/Almanack/life/trades/tradepri.cfm?showSite=mobile-regular

27 – PBS. *YouTube.com*, "Benjamin Franklin Makes a Name for Himself as a Printer | PBS | Ken Burns," April 4, 2022. https://www.youtube.com/watch?v=mAN9zW31Jdg

28 – *NPS.gov*, "Benjamin Franklin's Resume," https://www.nps.gov/inde/learn/historyculture/people-franklin-resume.htm

29 – Chris McManus. *Right Hand, Left Hand: The Origins of Asymmetry in Brains, Bodies, Atoms and Cultures* (Orion Publishing, 2003), page 348

30 – *Benjamin-Franklin-History.org*, "Timeline," http://www.benjamin-franklin-history.org/timeline/

31 – Charlie Rose. *YouTube.com*, "Walter Isaacson interview on Benjamin Franklin (2003)," February 10, 2017. https://www.youtube.com/watch?v=LMhOjS1L5Sw

32 – Meka Books. *YouTube.com*, "The Autobiography of Benjamin Franklin [Summary & Outline]," July 25, 2021. https://www.youtube.com/watch?v=7TLhT9MfFA4

33 – *CliffNotes.com*, "About The Autobiography of Benjamin Franklin," http://cliffsnotes.com/literature/a/the-autobiography-of-benjamin-franklin/about-the-autobiography-of-benjamin-franklin

34 – Evan Andrews. *History.com*, "11 Surprising Facts About Benjamin Franklin," August 19, 2020. https://www.history.com/news/11-surprising-facts-about-benjamin-franklin

35 – Independence Hall Association. *UShistory.org*, "Swim Fins," https://www.ushistory.org/franklin/science/swimfins.htm

36 – Kathleen Elkins. *CNBC.com*, "Here's when and why daylight saving time started in the US," March 6, 2020.

childhood, the 73-year-old Franklin had years to reflect on such a struggle. In doing so, he lists good justification for the equal use and development of both hands – a hallmark of any proud ambidexter. Would this fascinating man practice MMD if alive today? A close look at his Petition suggests that, yes, he would. Read the essay for yourself and see if you agree.

"A Petition of the Left Hand"

by Benjamin Franklin

To Those Who Have the Superintendency of Education,

I address myself to all the friends of youth and conjure them to direct their compassionate regards to my unhappy fate, in order to remove the prejudices of which I am the victim. There are twin sisters of us; and the two eyes of man do not more resemble, nor are capable of being upon better terms with each other, than my sister and myself, were it not for the partiality of our parents, who make the **most injurious distinctions between us**. From my infancy, I have been led to consider my sister as a being of a more elevated rank. I was suffered to grow up without the least instruction, while nothing was spared in her education. She had masters to teach her writing, drawing, music, and other accomplishments; but if by chance I touched a pencil, a pen, or a needle, I was bitterly rebuked; and more than once I have been beaten for being awkward and wanting a graceful manner. It is true, my sister associated me with her upon some occasions; but she always made a point of taking the lead, calling upon me only from necessity, or to figure by her side.

But conceive not, sirs, that my complaints are instigated merely by vanity. No; my uneasiness is occasioned by an object much more serious. It is the practice in our family, that the whole business of providing for its

Franklin excelled in many areas throughout his life, but what qualified him to make such an assertion to educators? Quite a bit, actually. Considered to be America's first millionaire,[18] Franklin once said, in reference to education, "If a man empties his purse into his head, no man can take it away from him. An investment in knowledge always pays the best interest."[19]

Figure 2.9: After retiring at 42, Franklin spent much of his time scientifically studying electricity, subsequently inventing the Lightning Rod. This made him an international celebrity

Even more, Franklin started what became America's first university after writing an essay in 1749 titled, Proposals Relating to the Education of Youth.[20] Using this essay, he organized 24 trustees to form an institution of higher education that challenged conventions of the day. Thirty years later, in 1779, this institution became the University of Pennsylvania. It was during this same year that Franklin wrote A Petition of the Left Hand. As if writing to his own, new university, Franklin addressed the essay "to those who have the Superintendency of Education."

Details from the essay mention the feminine left hand being beaten for attempting to make herself useful. From what sounds like the personification of an unforgettably unpleasant left-handed

https://www.cnbc.com/2019/03/08/when-and-why-daylight-saving-time-started-in-the-us.html

37 – 'Bobby.' *UPSbatteryCenter.com,* "Contribution of Benjamin Franklin to Electricity," June 6, 2014. https://www.upsbatterycenter.com/blog/contribution-benjamin-franklin-electricity/

LEONARDO DA VINCI

37 – *Wikipedia.org,* "Leonardo da Vinci," January 23, 2022. https://wikipedia.org/wiki/Leonardo_da_Vinci

38 – *Warehouse-13-Artifact-Database-Wiki.com,* "Leonardo da Vinci's Notebook," https://warehouse-13-artifact-database.fandom.com/wiki/Leonardo_da_Vinci%27s_Notebook

39 – Mindy Weisberger. *LiveScience.com,* "Leonardo Da Vinci Was Ambidextrous, Handwriting Analysis Shows," April 15, 2019. https://www.livescience.com/65225-da-vinci-ambidextrous.html

40 – Chris McManus. *Right Hand, Left Hand: The Origins of Asymmetry in Brains, Bodies, Atoms and Cultures* (Orion Publishing, 2003), pages 349–350

41 – Michael J. Lavery. *Whole Brain Power: The Fountain of Youth for the Mind and Body* (Lulu Press, 2008), page 137

42 – Memento Artem. *ClockTower.Ucollege.edu,* "Leonardo da Vinci: Corpse Caper," September 19, 2018. https://clocktower.ucollege.edu/articles/2018/leonardo-da-vinci-corpse-caper

43 – Ludwig Heinrich Heydenreich. *Britannica.com,* "Anatomical studies and drawings of Leonardo da Vinci," https://www.britannica.com/biography/Leonardo-da-Vinci/Anatomical-studies-and-drawings

44 – Jackie Craven. *ThoughtCo.com,* "Symmetry and Proportion in Design: What Leonardo Da Vinci Learned From Vitruvius," July 17, 2018. https://www.thoughtco.com/symmetry-and-proportion-in-design-177569

45 – *AirAndSpace.si.edu,* "Leonardo da Vinci's Codex on the Flight of Birds," October 22, 2013.
https://airandspace.si.edu/exhibitions/codex/

46 – *Da-Vinci-Inventions.com,* "Leonardo Da Vinci Inventions," 2019.
https://www.da-vinci-inventions.com/flying-machine

47 – *Wikipedia.org,* "Aristotle," March 29, 2022.
https://en.wikipedia.org/wiki/Aristotle

48 – *PalmariumArchive.com,* "Aristotle and Socrates on Beauty," July 12, 2013.
https://palmariumarchive.wordpress.com/2013/07/12/aristotle-and-socrates-on-beauty-im/

49 – Janice Bell. *Academia.edu,* "Aristotle as a Source for Leonardo's Theory of Colour Perspective after 1500," Journal of the Warburg and Courtauld Institutes. Vol 56. (1993) pp. 100-118. The Warburg Institute.
https://www.academia.edu/75260753/Aristotle_as_a_Source_for_Leonardos_Theory_of_Colour_Perspective_after_1500

50 – *Jefferson.edu,* "Was Leonardo Da Vinci's Dyslexia Responsible for His Brilliance?" May 7, 2019.
https://www.jefferson.edu/university/news/2019/05/7/dyslexia-helped-leonardo-davinci.html

51 – Brigit Katz. *SmithsonianMag.com,* "Was Leonardo da Vinci, a Famous Lefty, Actually Ambidextrous?" April 11, 2019.
https://www.smithsonianmag.com/smart-news/was-leonardo-da-vinci-famous-lefty-actually-ambidextrous-180971938/

52 – Michael J. Lavery. *Whole Brain Power: The Fountain of Youth for the Mind and Body* (Lulu Press, 2008), page 138

53 – Diego Irigoyen. *Creative Brain Training: Increase Attention Span, Build Confidence, and Stimulate Creativity* (Independently published, 2018), page 28

54 – Michael J. Lavery. *Whole Brain Power: The Fountain of Youth for the Mind and Body* (Lulu Press, 2008), page 152

When Baden-Powell, a man so dedicated to the equal understanding and balance of both sides of his body, died in 1941, he was buried near the center of where Earth's northern and southern hemispheres meet, a short distance from the Equator, in Nyeri, Kenya.

Benjamin Franklin

Figure 2.8: Franklin is one of history's foremost polymaths

One multilingual polymath who lived when using the left hand was considered unacceptable – even 'sinister,' – was Benjamin Franklin. Franklin became a household name through his various areas of expertise. He was a printer, publisher, businessman, diplomat, inventor, scientist, philosopher, U.S. Founding Father, and a writer.[14] His autobiography, although incomplete, became one of the most famous and influential of all time, recounting many of his life's personal details.[15] Within this work, though, Franklin never mentioned his own handedness, even though various sources consider him dual-dominant.[16]

It was while writing his autobiography that Franklin penned a separate essay called, A Petition of the Left Hand.[17] Like many of his essays, Franklin adopts a pseudonym, this one being a feminine characterization of the Left Hand. Written in 1779, Franklin's Petition creatively implores educators to stop forcing exclusive right-handedness – and instead, instruct the development of both hands.

heightened spatial awareness that was brought on by his own practice of MMD.[10] Even the very first knot a scout is required to learn – the square knot – is simple, symmetric, and tied using mirrored movement.[11] It is seen on the Scouting International logo, which features a symmetric fleur-de-lis – a shape that is drawn, ideally, using both hands.

Baden-Powell's enthusiasm for MMD, and desire to see it practiced by others, is demonstrated by his choice to make the official handshake of the Boy Scouts a simple, left-handed handshake.[12] In 1931, the Governor of Queensland, Lieutenant General Sir John Goodwin, recalled how Baden-

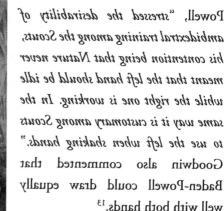

Figure 2.6: Scouting International logo: Symmetric, featuring the MMD-tied square knot

Figure 2.7: Baden-Powell writing left-handed

Powell," stressed the desirability of ambidextral training among the Scouts, his contention being that Nature never meant that the left hand should be idle while the right one is working. In the same way it is customary among Scouts to use the left when shaking hands." Goodwin also commented that Baden-Powell could draw equally well with both hands.[13]

55 – Leonardo da Vinci, translated by Jean Paul Richter (1888). *The Complete Notebooks of Leonardo da Vinci* (Eternal Sun Books, 2016), page 9

56 – *History.com,* "Leonardo da Vinci," December 2, 2009. https://www.history.com/topics/renaissance/leonardo-da-vinci

57 – Diego Irigoyen. *Creative Brain Training: Increase Attention Span, Build Confidence, and Stimulate Creativity* (Independently published, 2018), page 30

58 – 'Haunty.' *Owlcation.com,* "Leonardo da Vinci's Camera Obscura," December 22, 2016. https://owlcation.com/humanities/Leonardo-da-Vincis-Camera-Obscura

59 – Melissa Kelly. *ThoughtCo.com,* "Spatial Intelligence," May 30, 2019. https://www.thoughtco.com/spatial-intelligence-profile-8096

60 – Leonardo da Vinci, translated by Jean Paul Richter (1888). *The Complete Notebooks of Leonardo da Vinci* (Eternal Sun Books, 2016), page 26

61 – Diego Irigoyen. *Creative Brain Training: Increase Attention Span, Build Confidence, and Stimulate Creativity* (Independently published, 2018), page 43

62 – Darren Rousar. *SightSize.com,* "The Mirror – The Master of Painters," September 2021. https://www.sightsize.com/the-mirror-the-master-of-painters/

63 – Rachel Sult. *Cocre.co,* "Think Like a Genius: What Would Leonardo da Vinci Do with Today?" https://cocre.co/davinci-reflections/

64 – Pooja Shah. *Procaffenation.com,* "'Codex Leicester' The World's Most Expensive Book!" July 10, 2020. https://procaffenation.com/codex-leicester/

Chapter 3: The Science of MMD

1 – Queensland Brain Institute. *QBI.edu.au,* "Why our brain is the most intelligent machine of all," February 1, 2019.

https://qbi.uq.edu.au/article/2019/02/why-our-brain-most-intelligent-machine-all

2 – Tanya Lewis and Ashley P. Taylor. *LiveScience.com,* "Human brain: Facts, function & anatomy," May 28, 2021. https://www.livescience.com/29365-human-brain.html

3 – Todd Townes. *ShareCare.com,* "How many calories does the brain consume?" https://www.sharecare.com/health/calories/brain-calories-at-rest

4 – Meghan Jones. *RD.com,* "10 Fascinating Facts You Never Knew About Ambidextrous People," May 29, 2019. https://www.rd.com/list/facts-ambidextrous-people/

5 – David Wolman. *A Left-Hand Turn Around the World: Chasing the Mystery and Meaning of All Things Southpaw* (De Capo Press, 2005), page 48

6 – Vivian Lam. *ScopeBlog.Stanford.edu,* " "We know very little about the brain": Experts outline challenges in neuroscience," November 8, 2016. https://scopeblog.stanford.edu/2016/11/08/challenges-in-neuroscience-in-the-21st-century/

7 – Eero Vuoksimaa. *NCBI.NLM.NIH.gov,* "Origins of Handedness: A nationwide study of 30161 adults," January 16, 2009. https://www.ncbi.nlm.nih.gov/pmc/articles/PMC2680751/

8 – Olivia Guy-Evans. *SimplyPsychology.org,* "Lateralization of Brain Function," May 18, 2021. https://www.simplypsychology.org/brain-lateralization.html

9 – Michael Corballis. *ScientificAmerican.com,* "Can Training to Become Ambidextrous Improve Brain Function?" March 1, 2013. https://www.scientificamerican.com/article/can-training-to-become-ambidextrous-improve-brain-function/

10 – Kendra Cherry. *VeryWellMind.com,* "Left Brain Vs. Right Brain Dominance," April 10, 2020. https://www.verywellmind.com/left-brain-vs-right-brain-2795005

world, but they are likewise the preeminent agency by which we stamp our impress upon it. Moreover, and of equal import to the individual, it is by the movements of these members that the whole muscular tissues on both sides of the body are exercised, strengthened, and perfected.

"There is no doubt that the value of ambidexterity from a military point of view is immense. I do not consider a man is a thoroughly trained soldier unless he can mount equally well on either side of his horse, use the sword, pistol, and lance, equally well with both hands, and shoot off the left shoulder as rapidly and accurately as from the right.

"I wish I had cultivated in my youth the useful art of writing on two different subjects at once. I get through a great deal extra by using the right and left hand alternately, but I thoroughly appreciate how much more can be done by using them both together."

This Introduction ends with Baden-Powell signing his name, both, left- and right-handed.

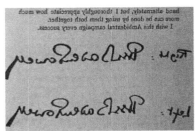

Figure 2.5: Baden-Powell's left- and right-handed signatures.

Baden-Powell is no exception to a polymathic tendency ambidexters have to excel in various fields,[8] as reflected in the introduction of merit badges – 57 of which were introduced to the Boy Scouts of America in its infancy.[9] These badges covered a vast spectrum of disciplines, ranging from Archery to Astronomy, Aviation to Business, Chemistry to Painting, Public Health to Sculpture, and many more. One can also argue that Baden-Powell's aptitude for knot tying, observation, and orienteering came from a

Baden-Powell was a practitioner and strong promoter of MMD.[6] A few years before starting the Boy Scouts, he served as Vice President of the Ambidextral Culture Society and wrote the introduction to their book — *Ambidexterity; Or Two-Handedness and Two-Brainedness, An Argument For Natural Development And Rational Education*. Written in 1905 by the organization's Secretary, John Jackson – a Scottish school teacher – *Ambidexterity* presents the science, history, and perceptions of dual-dominance as a beneficial practice to all.[7]

Figure 2.4: The official Scout Handshake is left-handed to develop dual-dominance

Within the book's Introduction, Baden-Powell tells us, "**I have long been accustomed to write with either hand or to use the two hands interchangeably.** To train the human body completely and **symmetrically**, that is, to cultivate all its organs and members to their utmost capacity, in order that its functions may also attain their **maximum development**, is an obligation that cannot safely be ignored. This completeness and symmetry can only be secured by an equal attention to, and exercise of, both sides of the body – the right and the left; and this **two-sided growth can alone be promoted and matured by educating our two hands equally**, each in precisely the same way, and exactly to the same extent.

"Our hands – and our arms, from which, for purposes both of argument and education, they cannot be separated – not only constitute our chief medium of communication with the outer

11 – "Grand Wanderer." *Instructables.com,* "How to Develop Ambidexterity," 2013. https://www.instructables.com/How-to-Develop-Ambidexterity/

12 – Andreas Roller. *BlurbSlate.com,* "Are the pedals the same in a left hand drive car?" March 3, 2021. https://blurbslate.com/are-the-pedals-the-same-in-a-left-hand-drive-car

13 – Michael J. Lavery. *Whole Brain Power: The Fountain of Youth for the Mind and Body* (Lulu Press, 2008), page 50

14 – Allison Wild. *BuzzFeed.com,* "17 Everyday Objects That Are Useless To Left-Handed People," July 18, 2017. https://www.buzzfeed.com/allisonwild/its-a-righty-word-were-just-living-in-it

15 – Tracey le Roux. *OT-Mom-Learning-Activities.com,* "Is Your Child Switching Hands?" https://www.ot-mom-learning-activities.com/switching-hands.html

16 – Michael J. Lavery. *Whole Brain Power: The Fountain of Youth for the Mind and Body* (Lulu Press, 2008), page 204

17 – Chris McManus. *Right Hand, Left Hand: The Origins of Asymmetry in Brains, Bodies, Atoms and Cultures* (Orion Publishing, 2003), page 179

18 – Multiple Contributors. Reviewed by Dan Brennan, MD. *WebMD.com,* "The Difference Between the Left and Right Brain," April 15, 2021. https://www.webmd.com/brain/the-difference-between-the-left-and-right-brain

19 – Michael J. Lavery. *Whole Brain Power: The Fountain of Youth for the Mind and Body* (Lulu Press, 2008), page xii

20 – Chris McManus. *Right Hand, Left Hand: The Origins of Asymmetry in Brains, Bodies, Atoms and Cultures* (Orion Publishing, 2003), page 242

21 – Ibid., page 238

22 – Michael J. Lavery. *Whole Brain Power: The Fountain of Youth for the Mind and Body* (Lulu Press, 2008), page 54

23 – Ibid., page 138

24 – Ibid., page 55

25 – Ibid., page 61

26 – Ibid., page 147

27 – Ibid., page 143

28 – David Wolman. *A Left-Hand Turn Around the World: Chasing the Mystery and Meaning of All Things Southpaw* (De Capo Press, 2005), page 120

29 – Ibid., page 127

30 – Ibid., page 194

31 – Michael J. Lavery. *Whole Brain Power: The Fountain of Youth for the Mind and Body* (Lulu Press, 2008), page 57

32 – Robert H. Shmerling, MD. *Health.Harvard.edu,* "Right brain/left brain, right?" November 8, 2019. https://www.health.harvard.edu/blog/right-brainleft-brain-right-2017082512222

33 – David Wolman. *A Left-Hand Turn Around the World: Chasing the Mystery and Meaning of All Things Southpaw* (De Capo Press, 2005), pages 192 & 196

34 – Ibid., page 49

35 – Michael J. Lavery. *Whole Brain Power: The Fountain of Youth for the Mind and Body* (Lulu Press, 2008), page 143

36 – Ibid., page 155

37 – Ibid., page 152

38 – Diego Irigoyen. *Creative Brain Training: Increase Attention Span, Build Confidence, and Stimulate Creativity* (Independently published, 2018), page 21

39 – Michael J. Lavery. *Whole Brain Power: The Fountain of Youth for the Mind and Body* (Lulu Press, 2008), page 153

40 – Ibid., page 154

In 1899, Baden-Powell commanded a garrison of 217 troops to defend a town from 8,000 Boer army soldiers during the Siege of Mafeking in South Africa.[2] This made him a hero back in England, and earned him a promotion to Major-General by Queen Victoria.[3] He also had a three-year post as a spy on the Island of Malta. There, he disguised himself as an entomologist and hid secret details of enemy fortifications and elevation contours within his drawings of leaves, moths, and butterflies.[4]

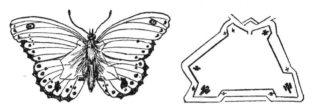

Figure 2.3: As a spy, Baden-Powell concealed details of enemy fortresses inside his nature drawings, like at the center of this symmetric butterfly (secret details of corner guns and cannons expanded at right)

Baden-Powell descriptively wove his many skills together in writing. His most famous book, Scouting for Boys, was used by British teachers and community leaders to instruct youth. It became the fourth best-selling book of the 20th century and, inadvertently, started the international movement known as the Boy Scouts.[5]

By the end of 1910, a mere three years after holding his first camp of just 22 boys on Brownsea Island, there were over 100,000 Scouts in England. Baden-Powell retired from the Army to focus exclusively on promoting Scouting. By 1922, there were more than a million scouts in 32 countries. By 1939, the number of Scouts had grown to over 3 million.

Lord Robert Baden-Powell

Figure 2.1: Baden-Powell becomes a national hero after defending the town of Mafeking in South Africa

Figure 2.2: World War I poster art created by Baden-Powell

Baden-Powell shared his many skills with the youth – teaching them self-discipline, leadership, and education on the wonders of our natural world. Baden-Powell's past includes serving as a British General, Crown spy, author, artist, musician, and Founder of the international Scouting movement. Born in 1857, Baden-Powell's love of nature often led him to sneak out of school and spend time in the woods. There, he would observe nature, hunt for food, hike, canoe, and hone survival skills. These later became a key focus of the Boy Scouts.[1]

41 – Olivia Guy-Evans. *SimplyPsychology.org*, "Broca's Area Function and Location," June 28, 2021. https://www.simplypsychology.org/broca-area.html

42 – Jason G. Goldman. *BBC.com*, "Evolution: Why are most of us right-handed?" December 15, 2014. https://www.bbc.com/future/article/20141215-why-are-most-of-us-right-handed

43 – Michael J. Lavery. *Whole Brain Power: The Fountain of Youth for the Mind and Body* (Lulu Press, 2008), page 101

44 – Chris McManus. *Right Hand, Left Hand: The Origins of Asymmetry in Brains, Bodies, Atoms and Cultures* (Orion Publishing, 2003), page 348

45 – Katja Guenther. *NCBI.NLM.NIH.gov*, "'It's All Done With Mirrors': V.S. Ramachandran and the Material Culture of Phantom Limb Research," July 2016. https://www.ncbi.nlm.nih.gov/pmc/articles/PMC4904333/

46 – Rachael Lowe. *Physio-pedia.com*, "Mirror Therapy," February 3,2022. https://www.physio-pedia.com/Mirror_Therapy

47 – Thomas Politzer, O.D. *BrainLine.org*, "Vision Is Our Dominant Sense," July 26, 2018. https://www.brainline.org/article/vision-our-dominant-sense

48 – Patrick Cohn. *PeakSports.com*, "Sports Visualization: The Secret Weapon of Athletes" https://www.peaksports.com/sports-psychology-blog/sports-visualization-athletes/

49 – Anastasia Haralabidou. *Virgin.com*, "Great ideas: Is imagination more important than knowledge," February 12, 2015. https://www.virgin.com/about-virgin/latest/great-ideas-imagination-more-important-knowledge

Chapter 4: The Benefits of MMD

1 – Dr. Thomas Ball. *PerformanceHealthCenter.com*, "Use Your Left Hand to Be in Your Right Mind," Februart 28, 2019.

https://performancehealthcenter.com/2019/02/use-your-left-hand-to-be-in-your-right-mind/

2 – *Beat-Fitness.com*, "Non-Dominant Side Training," https://www.beat-fitness.com/non-dominant-side-training/

3 – Michael J. Lavery. *Whole Brain Power: The Fountain of Youth for the Mind and Body* (Lulu Press, 2008), page 136

4 – Diego Irigoyen. *Creative Brain Training: Increase Attention Span, Build Confidence, and Stimulate Creativity* (Independently published, 2018), page 20

5 – Bob Yirka. *Phys.org*, "Left and right brain hemispheres found to store memory differently in ants," May 6, 2020. https://phys.org/news/2020-05-left-brain-hemispheres-memories-differently.html

6 – David Wolman. *A Left-Hand Turn Around the World: Chasing the Mystery and Meaning of All Things Southpaw* (De Capo Press, 2005), page 129

7 – Anthony Metivier. *MagneticMemoryMethod.com*, "Ambidextrousness and Memory: Can Dual Handedness Boost Your Brain?" April 7, 2021. https://www.magneticmemorymethod.com/ambidextrousness/

8 – John Jackson. *Ambidexterity: Or Two-Handedness and Two-Brainedness, An Argument For Natural Development And Rational Education.* (Dryden House London, 1905), page 133

9 – Michael J. Lavery. *Whole Brain Power: The Fountain of Youth for the Mind and Body* (Lulu Press, 2008), page 21

10 – *PsichologyAnswers.com*, "What is the meaning of spatial reasoning?" https://psichologyanswers.com/library/lecture/read/554926-what-is-the-meaning-of-spatial-reasoning

11 – Steve Steinberg. *WebMD.com*, "Strengthen the Nondominant Side of Your Body" https://www.webmd.com/fitness-exercise/features/strengthen-the-nondominant-side-of-your-body#1

CHAPTER 2

The Big Three: Da Vinci, Franklin, and Baden-Powell

While the previous MMD practitioners showcased exceptional skill throughout their lives, three historic individuals (aka the Big 3) provide us with additional details into their relationship with MMD – Lord Robert Baden-Powell, Benjamin Franklin, and Leonardo da Vinci.

- **Lord Robert Baden-Powell**, the 19th-century British General, royal spy, founder of the Boy Scouts, and real-life Indiana Jones wrote, "To train the human body completely and symmetrically…is an obligation that cannot safely be ignored."
- **Benjamin Franklin** was courted by kings as one of the most interesting men of the 18th century. His accomplishments in science, literature, diplomacy, business, and civic development remain influential to this day. Franklin wrote of the need to equally educate and develop both hands.
- **Leonardo da Vinci** mastered architecture, engineering, mechanics, and painting as the greatest creative of the Italian Renaissance. Da Vinci wrote with both hands in various directions, including traditional, mirrored, and inverted.

12 – Michael J. Lavery. *Whole Brain Power: The Fountain of Youth for the Mind and Body* (Lulu Press, 2008), page xvi

13 – Jim Houliston. *YouTube.com*, "Urban Rail Walking – URW" channel.
https://www.youtube.com/channel/UC7kg_vI6XIDfA91Piz1QTJw

14 – Michael J. Lavery. *Whole Brain Power: The Fountain of Youth for the Mind and Body* (Lulu Press, 2008), page 153

15 – Michael J. Lavery. *YouTube.com*, "Ambidextrous Pitcher Chuck Mellick," June 23, 2008.
https://www.youtube.com/watch?v=xTzDJFbH91w

16 – Michael J. Lavery. *Whole Brain Power: The Fountain of Youth for the Mind and Body* (Lulu Press, 2008), page 213

17 – Ibid., page 210

18 – Diego Irigoyen. *Lettering-Daily.com*, "How to Become Ambidextrous in 6 Easy Steps," https://www.lettering-daily.com/6-steps-to-become-ambidextrous/

19 – Diego Irigoyen. *Creative Brain Training: Increase Attention Span, Build Confidence, and Stimulate Creativity* (Independently published, 2018), page 7

20 – Courtney E. Ackerman, M.A. *PositivePsychology.com*, "What is Neuroplasticity? A Psychologist Explains," May 2, 2022.
https://positivepsychology.com/neuroplasticity/

21 – Jim Houliston. *YouTube.com*, "Extended Interview with Ebiye Jeremy, Captain of Team USA Beach Handball," September 21, 2021.
https://www.youtube.com/watch?v=Gldw-kJO4Gg

22 – Jim Houliston. *YouTube.com*, "My MMD Lifestyle – Jim Houliston," January 12, 2022.
https://www.youtube.com/watch?v=mFf_14lND1A&t=1059s

23 – Jim Houliston. *YouTube.com*, "Interview with Dr. Kathryn Ko, Ambidextrous Neurosurgeon and Fine Artist," September 21, 2021.
https://www.youtube.com/watch?v=OR_1pFj9lTs&t=5s

24 – Sandra Levy. *HealthLine.com,* "Walking May Boost Your Creativity," October 20, 2018. healthline.com/health-news/walking-indoors-outdoors-increases-creativity-042814

25 – Ekua Hagan. *PsychologyToday.com,* "Einstein's Genius Linked to Well-Connected Brain Hemispheres," October 5, 2013. https://www.psychologytoday.com/us/blog/the-athletes-way/201310/einsteins-genius-linked-well-connected-brain-hemispheres

26 – Diego Irigoyen. *Lettering-Daily.com,* "How to Become Ambidextrous in 6 Easy Steps," https://www.lettering-daily.com/6-steps-to-become-ambidextrous/

27 – Dr. Thomas Ball. *PerformanceHealthCenter.com,* "Use Your Left Hand to Be in Your Right Mind," Februart 28, 2019. https://performancehealthcenter.com/2019/02/use-your-left-hand-to-be-in-your-right-mind/

28 – *AnatomyTrains.com,* "A Brief History of Anatomy Trains," https://www.anatomytrains.com/about-us/history/

29 – Giovanni Roselli. *WeckMethod.com,* "Non-Dominant Side Training Tips to Elevate Your Performance," April 8, 2016. https://www.weckmethod.com/articles/non-dominant-side-training-tips-to-elevate-your-performance

30 – Beverly Hosford. *AceFitness.org,* "10 Daily Habits That Can Cause Muscular Imbalances," December 4, 2015. https://www.acefitness.org/education-and-resources/professional/expert-articles/5760/10-daily-habits-that-can-cause-muscular-imbalances/

31 – John Murphy. *MDLinx.com,* "5 sports scientifically proven to help you live longer," April 20, 2020. https://www.mdlinx.com/article/5-sports-scientifically-proven-to-help-you-live-longer/Uby97i7J2o4tB63pEy0zB

32 – Andrew Treddinick. *DailyOrange.com,* "TENNIS: Orange confuses opponents with ambidextrous serving," February 8, 2011. *dailyorange.com/2011/02/tennis-orange-confuses-opponents-with-ambidextrous-serving/*

handedness survey for draftsmen and graphic artists. In the survey, Escher asked questions related to dual-dominance and advanced spatial awareness. Questions included, "*Aside from with the left hand, can you also draw, engrave and cut with the right one effortlessly (e.g. a human profile rotated to the left with the right hand just as easily as a profile rotated to the right with the left)?*"

Figure 1.17: Jimi Hendrix played guitar lefty but was forced to play righty by his dad. He also performed various tasks using alternate hands

Electric guitar legend, Jimi Hendrix, preferred different hands for different tasks. His left hand was used to play his right-handed guitar upside down, throw, comb his hair, and hold cigarettes.[52] His right was used for writing, eating, and talking on the phone. Hendrix's father believed that left-handed guitar playing was a sign of the devil. To prevent having his guitar taken away, Hendrix learned to play right-handed whenever his dad was present.[53]

brain 'growing' activity), then shouldn't his brain be physically larger than average? Perhaps not. MMD may increase brain efficiency more than physical weight or mass. This would be comparable to a Ferrari weighing less than a Toyota, while still performing much faster.

The Indian civil rights activist, **Mahatma Gandhi**, was a dominant right-hander who developed the ability to write lefty to become not solely dependent on his right hand.[50]

The visual master of otherworldly graphic design, M.C. Escher, developed dual-dominance at a young age.[51] He was forced to write and draw right-handed in school. Escher wrote, *"I was exclusively left-handed from my earliest childhood. At primary school I found learning to write with my right hand extremely difficult. I would probably have managed to write in mirror image with my left hand far more easily and naturally."*

Escher followed in the footsteps of his teacher, **Samuel Jessurun de Mesquita**, who also developed dual-dominance. As a graphic artist dealing with both traditional- and mirrored-image,

Figure 1.16: M.C. Escher preferred using his left hand, but was forced to use his right hand in school

Escher's ambidexterity proved highly valuable for creating stunning works of spatially mesmerizing art. In 1953, Escher produced a left-

33 – *Wikipedia.org*, "Gordie Howe," February 1, 2022.
https://wikipedia.org/wiki/Gordie_Howe

34 – Del Milligan. *TheLedger.com*, "Being an Ambidextrous Golfer
Means Twice the Holes-in-One," March 12, 2013.
https://www.theledger.com/story/news/2013/03/11/being-an-
ambidextrous-golfer-means-twice-the-holes-in-one/26858922007/

Chapter 5: Mirror Reading

1 – *Wikipedia.org*, "Language," January 20, 2022.
https://en.wikipedia.org/wiki/Language

2 – Steph Koyfman. *Babbel.com*, "Why Is Most Language Read From
Left To Right?" April 28, 2021.
https://www.babbel.com/en/magazine/right-to-left-languages

3 – *MirrorRead.com*, "About Us,"
https://www.mirrorread.com/our_team

4 – *MirrorRead.com*, "Frequently Asked Questions,"
https://www.mirrorread.com/faq

5 – R.A. Poldrack, J.E. Desmond, G.H. Glover, and J.D. Gabrieli.
Academic.oup.com, "The neural basis of visual skill learning: an fMRI
study of mirror reading," January 1, 1998.
https://academic.oup.com/cercor/article/8/1/1/339758

6 – B. Deweer, B. Pillon, A. Michon, and B. Dubois. *TandFonline.com*,
"Mirror reading in Alzheimer's disease: Normal skill learning and
acquisition of item-specific information," January 4, 2008.
https://www.tandfonline.com/doi/abs/10.1080/01688639308402596

7 – Dr. Shelagh Robinson. *MirrorRead.com*, "Sweet Mysteries of Mirror
Reading," https://www.mirrorread.com/single-post/2018/01/11/sweet-
mysteries-of-mirror-reading

8 – Emma G. Duerden and Daniele Laverdure-Dupont. *JneuroSci.org*,
"Practice Makes Cortex," August 27, 2008.
https://www.jneurosci.org/content/jneuro/28/35/8655.full.pdf

9 – *MirrorRead.com,* "Frequently Asked Questions,"
https://www.mirrorread.com/faq

suffered a stroke that weakened his right side. With only a little practice, Wilson started writing fluently with his left hand and continued to do so for the next year.[44]

While he was only ever photographed writing with his right hand, **Albert Einstein** had an abnormally symmetric brain. This feature produces greater connections between both brain hemispheres and typically occurs among the ambidextrous.[45] At autopsy, it was discovered that Einstein's brain had a thicker corpus callosum[46] and an exceptional number of glial cells. The corpus callosum serves as the communication bridge between our two brain hemispheres while glial cells are responsible for the speed of cognition. The more glial cells one has,

Figure 1.13: Houdini practiced dual-dominance to become a better magician

the higher their native intelligence.[47] Einstein's genius is often associated with a highly creative imagination – considered a right-brain function exercised by left-sided body movement.[48]

When talking about Einstein and his brain, it is important to clarify MMD-induced brain growth. Einstein's brain weighed 10% less than the average adult, at only 2.7 pounds.[49] If Einstein practiced a spectrum of MMD (a

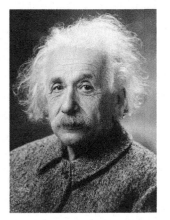

Figure 1.14: Einstein's brain shows evidence of dual-dominance

now, but then I was left-handed and had comparatively little strength in my right arm."[38]

Figure 1.11: President Garfield wrote with both hands and was multilingual

The brilliant, yet overlooked, 20th U.S. President, **James Garfield**, mastered several languages and was the first president to campaign bilingually – in both English and German. He also developed the ability to use one hand to write Latin while, simultaneously, using the other hand to write Greek.[39]

It was a tutor named **Edwin Henry Landseer who taught England's Queen Victoria** the use of both hands. Landseer demonstrated his talent by drawing the head of a horse with one hand and the head of a buck with the other, simultaneously.[40]

Illusionist and escape artist **Harry Houdini** trained himself to become dual-dominant to better handle cards,[41] escape chains and straitjackets while hanging upside down, and generally outdo his competitor's performances.[42] Houdini even encouraged dual-dominant training for all children.[43]

In 1896, while still a professor at Princeton University, 28th U.S. President, **Woodrow Wilson**,

Figure 1.12: Queen Victoria was taught to use both hands by her ambidextrous tutor

PICTURE CREDITS

Introduction

X.1 – Public Domain
https://commons.wikimedia.org/wiki/File:Ambidextrie.svg

Chapter 1: History's Spectrum of MMD

1.1 – Creative Commons. Authors: Patrick J. Lynch, Medical
Illustrator, and C. Carl Jaffe, MD, Cardiologist.
https://commons.wikimedia.org/wiki/File:Skeleton_anterior.svg

1.2 – Graphic text by Jim Houliston
https://ambilifeorg.files.wordpress.com/2022/03/picsart_03-14-
04.31.36.jpg

1.3 – Creative Commons. Author: Penarc
https://commons.wikimedia.org/wiki/File:Rongo_rongo_Tafel.jpg

1.4 – Public Domain
https://en.wikipedia.org/wiki/File:Mirror_writing2.jpg

1.5 – Creative Commons. Author: Marie-Lan Nguyen
https://commons.wikimedia.org/wiki/File:Plato_Silanion_Musei_Capit
olini_MC1377.jpg

1.6 – Public Domain
https://commons.wikimedia.org/wiki/File:God2-Sistine_Chapel.png

1.7 – Public Domain
https://commons.wikimedia.org/wiki/File:Mozart-small.jpg

1.8 – Public Domain
https://commons.wikimedia.org/wiki/File:Thomas_Jefferson_by_Rembrandt_Peale,_1800.jpg

1.9 – Public Domain
https://commons.wikimedia.org/wiki/File:Lewis_Carroll_1863.jpg

1.10 – Public Domain
https://commons.wikimedia.org/wiki/File:Tesla3.jpg

1.11 – Public Domain
https://commons.wikimedia.org/wiki/File:GARFIELD,_James_A-President_(BEP_engraved_portrait).jpg

1.12 – Public Domain
https://commons.wikimedia.org/wiki/File:Queen_Victoria_1887_(Cropped).jpg

1.13 – Public Domain
https://commons.wikimedia.org/wiki/File:HandCuffHarryHoudini.jpg

1.14 – Public Domain
https://commons.wikimedia.org/wiki/File:Albert_Einstein_Head.jpg

1.15 – Public Domain
https://commons.wikimedia.org/wiki/File:Gandhi,_studio_picture,_1931.jpg

1.16 – Creative Commons. Author: Pedro Ribeiro Simões
https://commons.wikimedia.org/wiki/File:The_Artist_-Maurits_Cornelelius_Escher-_working_at_his_Atelier_(50385403156).jpg

1.17 – Public Domain
https://commons.wikimedia.org/wiki/File:Jimi-Hendrix-1967-Helsinki.jpg

Chapter 2: The Big Three – Da Vinci, Franklin, and Baden-Powell

2.1 – Public Domain
https://commons.wikimedia.org/wiki/File:Baden_Powell.jpg

of the specimens are written in a beautiful manner. All are good. The writing in nearly all cases slants backwards instead of forward."[32] **The dual-dominant polymath and renaissance man, Sir Daniel Wilson,** was knighted by Queen Victoria as a gifted artist, historian, ethnologist, poet, author, archaeologist, literary critic, and museum maker.[33] After nearly 80 years of ambidextral development, Wilson stated, "Experience shows that wherever the early and persistent cultivation of the full use of both hands has been carried out, the result is greater efficiency, without any counterbalancing effect. We are bimanous in the best sense, and are meant to have the free, unrestrained use of both hands."[34]

Alice in Wonderland author, **Lewis Carroll,** wrote over 100,000 letters to his adoring fans, and many of them were quite special.[35] Called "looking-glass letters," these were written by Carroll in mirrored script.[36] Even Carroll's illustrator, **Peter Newell,** dabbled with mirrored script when creating the earliest known, non-natural, rotational ambigram – a style of calligraphy with multiple spatial interpretations.[37]

In his autobiography, inventor and futurist **Nikola Tesla** described himself this way – "I am ambidextrous

Figure 1.9: Lewis Carroll wrote various letters in mirrored direction

Figure 1.10: Nikola Tesla described himself as ambidextrous

Albert Einstein to become a master violinist.[28]

Before becoming the 3rd U.S. President, the multilingual **Thomas Jefferson was sent by** Congress in 1784 to join Benjamin Franklin in France for commercial negotiations. Two years later, while still in France, Jefferson broke his right wrist. The accident forced him to begin writing with his left hand while the other rehabilitated. Jefferson continued developing dual-dominance for the remainder of his life... another 40 years![29]

Figure 1.8: Thomas Jefferson taught himself to write left-handed after injuring his right wrist

The surgical pioneer and professor, Dr. **Thomas Dent Mütter,** who taught fellow surgeons years ahead of him, was considered the best in his profession. As a young surgeon in the 1830's, his ambidextrous skills astounded amphitheaters of students, surgeons, and onlookers who could not tell just which hand to follow – baffled at how they could ever replicate his otherworldly skills.[30] The doctor also collected a vast array of medical oddities, all of which can be viewed today inside his Mütter Museum in Philadelphia, Pennsylvania. This museum is also the only place in the world to have on public display slides from the brain of Albert Einstein, which will be discussed more in this chapter.[31]

American poet, Walt Whitman, described in his 1866 piece, Left-hand writing by soldiers, the clarity of less-dominant handwriting samples from U.S. **Civil War soldier amputees** who had quickly learned the skill out of necessity. Whitman wrote that, "a great many

2.2 – Public Domain
https://commons.wikimedia.org/wiki/File:%27Are_you_in_this%27_p
oster.jpg

2.3 – Public Domain
https://www.gutenberg.org/files/15715/15715-h/images/

2.4 – Creative Commons. Author: GeorgeLouis
https://commons.wikimedia.org/wiki/File:Leaders_welcoming_boy_int
o_Mexico_Scouting.jpg

2.5 – Public Domain
https://ambilifeorg.files.wordpress.com/2022/04/20220412_084559.jpg

2.6 – Creative Commons. Author: Matthewaptaylor
https://commons.wikimedia.org/wiki/File:Scouts_Aotearoa_Logo.svg

2.7 – Public Domain
https://commons.m.wikimedia.org/wiki/File:Robert_Baden-
Powell_(von_Herkomer).jpg

2.8 – Public Domain
https://commons.wikimedia.org/wiki/File:BenFranklinDuplessis.jpg

2.9 – Public Domain
https://commons.wikimedia.org/wiki/File:HD.11.029_(10995364195)
.jpg

2.10 – Typesetting on display at the Benjamin Franklin Museum in
Philadelphia, National Park Service. Photo taken by Jim Houliston.
https://ambilifeorg.files.wordpress.com/2022/03/screenshot_20220120
-082837_gallery.jpg

2.11 – Public Domain
https://commons.wikimedia.org/wiki/File:Benjamin_Franklin_1767.jpg

2.12 – "The Bond" statue of Franklin and Washington in Philadelphia
by artist Jim West. Photo by Jim Houliston.
https://ambilifeorg.files.wordpress.com/2022/03/screenshot_20220120
-091855_gallery.jpg

2.13 – Public Domain
https://commons.wikimedia.org/wiki/File:Portrait_of_Leonardo_da_Vi
nci_(from_Characaturas_by_Leonardo_da_Vinci,_from_Drawings_by

_Wincelslaus_Hollar,_out_of_the_Portland_Museum)_MET_DP8241
04.jpg

2.14 – Public Domain
https://commons.wikimedia.org/wiki/File:Da_Vinci_mirror_writing.jp
g

2.15 – Public Domain
https://commons.wikimedia.org/wiki/File:De_divina_proportione_-
_Illustration_05.jpg

2.16 – Graphic by Jim Houliston
https://ambilifeorg.files.wordpress.com/2022/04/davinciquote.jpg

2.17 – Creative Commons. Author: Crijam
https://commons.wikimedia.org/wiki/File:L%C3%A9onard_de_Vinci,
_Bille_de_verre_et_%C5%93il_humain,_vers_1508-
09,_MS_D,_3v.jpg

2.18 – Public Domain
https://commons.wikimedia.org/wiki/File:0_The_Vitruvian_Man_-
_by_Leonardo_da_Vinci.jpg

Chapter 3: The Science of MMD

3.1 – Public Domain
https://commons.wikimedia.org/wiki/File:02_1_facies_dorsalis_cere
bri.jpg

3.2 – Creative Commons. Author: Terry Presley
https://www.flickr.com/photos/36979785@N06/6187072323/

3.3 – Photo by Jim Houliston
https://ambilifeorg.files.wordpress.com/2022/03/picsart_09-24-
09.53.47.jpg

3.4 – Public Domain
https://commons.wikimedia.org/wiki/File:US_Navy_110302-N-
9094S-
060_Ship%27s_Serviceman_Seaman_Krista_Stelzner_draws_pictures_
with_a_child_during_a_community_service_event.jpg

performing them with each hand and with both together—for they are both alike—your object being ready to attain ability, grace, speed, painlessness, elegance and readiness."[24]

Figure 1.6: Michelangelo used both hands to paint the Sistine Chapel

In the first century CE, **Celsus**, a Roman physician, encouraged dual-dominance for surgeons, saying they should be "ready to use the left hand as well as the right."[25]

Figure 1.7: Mozart composed music with both hands

Italian Renaissance genius, **Michelangelo**, painted his masterpiece, the Sistine Chapel ceiling, using both hands.[26] He also chose to portray Adam extending his left hand towards God.

Austrian classical composer, **Wolfgang Amadeus Mozart**, composed music with both his left and right hands.[27] Centuries later, his music would inspire

characteristics that may have been augmented by the brain-growing practice of MMD. Namely, they were:

- **Polymaths** who excelled in multiple, unrelated disciplines, ranging from science to art to math and music.
- **Luminaries** who inspired their fellow man and catalyzed large-scale cultural changes.
- **Naturephiles** who observed and cherished and created order.

Figure 1.5: Plato and Hippocrates praised and promoted dual-dominance

Before we take a deeper dive into our "Big 3," and explore their notable standings on the MMD spectrum, here are some more honorable mentions:

The 4th-century BCE Greek philosopher, teacher, and founder of the first institution of higher education in the Western world,[21] **Plato**, was convinced that the limbs are naturally of equal strength, balance, and ability. He believed that dominant handedness was not part of our physical design, but rather a cultural impartation created by our caregivers', misguided habit of exclusivity.[22] Plato also praised the ancient Scythian archers for their ability to shoot equally from both sides of the body.[23]

The Father of Modern Medicine and Plato contemporary, **Hippocrates**, urged his patients to *"practice all the operations,*

15

3.5 – Creative Commons. Author: Anatomography, Life Science Databases(LSDB). "Corpus Callosum"
https://commons.wikimedia.org/wiki/File:Corpus_callosum.png

3.6 – Public Domain
https://commons.wikimedia.org/wiki/File:Brain_Exercising.png

3.7 – Frontiers in Neurology. December 11, 2020. Editor: Nicola Smania.
https://www.frontiersin.org/articles/10.3389/fneur.2020.568261/full

3.8 – Photo by Jim Houliston
https://ambilifeorg.files.wordpress.com/2022/03/picsart_01-22-06.15.53.jpg

Chapter 4: The Benefits of MMD

4.1 – Creative Commons. Author: Nickbyrd
https://commons.wikimedia.org/wiki/File:Thinker_mri.jpg

4.2 – Photo by Brad Morris
https://ambilifeorg.files.wordpress.com/2022/03/screenshot_20220110-201903_gallery.jpg

4.3 – Public Domain
https://commons.wikimedia.org/wiki/File:Waist_measurement.jpg

4.4 – Public Domain
https://www.loc.gov/pictures/item/2002723319/

4.5 – Public Domain
https://commons.wikimedia.org/wiki/File:Gordie_Howe_Chex_card.jpg

Chapter 5: Mirror Reading

5.1 – Creative Commons. Author: Basile Morin
https://commons.wikimedia.org/wiki/File:Ambigram_Magic_Dream_-_mirror_symmetry_with_a_handheld_pattern_giving_a_reversed_shadow_on_a_blue_wall.jpg

5.2 – Photo by Shelagh Robinson

https://ambilifeorg.files.wordpress.com/2022/03/dr-shelagh-robinson.jpg

5.3 – Creative Commons. Author: Basile Morin
https://commons.wikimedia.org/wiki/File:Ambigram_Body_Yoga,_mirror_symmetry.png

5.4 – Graphic by Jim Houliston
https://ambilifeorg.files.wordpress.com/2022/03/screenshot_20220123-143232_gallery-e1647970072857.jpg

Figure 1.4: Symmetric calligraphy of the Ottoman Empire

Great Britain's Queen Victoria practiced MMD before the Ambidextral Culture Society was founded within her own country. Through this group, hundreds of people worked to develop dual-dominance, many of whom were doctors, surgeons, professors, and students.[16] One of these practitioners was the world-famous Lord Robert Baden-Powell.

The society influenced U.S. cities like Philadelphia[17] and Boston,[18] where school teachers demonstrated and instructed students to develop dual-dominance. Major League Baseball even had four ambidextrous pitchers during this time.[19] The era's Victorian novelist, Charles Reade, also wrote brashly that, "every child is even and either handed till some grown fool interferes and mutilates it."[20]

With additional practitioners like Plato, Hippocrates, Michelangelo, Mozart, Gandhi, Houdini, Hendrix, and more, you will see a variety of famous, historic people practicing a spectrum of MMD and experiencing robust benefits.

The "BIG 3" of Da Vinci, Franklin, and Baden-Powell are unique in their claims, observations, and practices relating to use of the less-dominant side. They also embodied a few notable

14

Figure 1.2). Switching hands between lines is the ideal way to write boustrophedon. Try it with a simple paragraph. This activity, like all MMD, equally exercises both sides of the brain and body.[10]

Ancient historians like Josephus, Pliny, Justin, and Herodotus wrote of the **Scythians**: a flourishing civilization known for their physical longevity, strength, and military success. It is recorded that the Scythian culture legally instituted the practice of MMD in all their activities.[11]

Figure 1.3: Rongorongo: the dual-dominant writing style of the Easter Islanders

As early as the 17th century, the **Easter Islanders** had their own dual-dominant, biscriptal writing style with rongorongo.[12] It was similar to boustrophedon, but with an additional element: inverted alternating lines. Two centuries earlier, on the other side of the world, Leonardo da Vinci was filling his own personal notebooks with, both, mirrored and inverted writing.[13]

The 18th-century **Ottomans** practiced MMD through their mystical, mirrored calligraphy.[14]

The late 19th century was a notable time for MMD in the world, particularly in **Great Britain, Japan, Persia,** and **the United States.**[15]

INDEX

Could it be that the timeless practice of MMD is actually the more practical, intuitive, and holistic approach to body mechanics and human development? Considering the bilaterally symmetric design of an average human skeleton, exterior sensory features (eyes, ears, hands, feet, etc.), and weight distribution of the entire organic system, what can be accomplished by one side of our body, can be accomplished by the other side equally – if taught.[4]

Most young children instinctively practice MMD.[5] As they learn to kick, throw, reach, and turn to grab objects, both sides of the body engage. If their development is not hindered, some children begin writing in mirrored and even inverted direction with both hands.[6] Leonardo da Vinci, as we shall see, practiced this skill his entire life.

"If you would not be forgotten as soon as you are dead and rotten, either write things worth reading or do things worth writing". -Benjamin Franklin

Figure 1.2: Modern example of boustrophedon: the handwriting style of ancient Greece

Let's take a look at various civilizations and cultures who practiced MMD throughout history:

The ancient Greeks were one of the most advanced civilizations our world has ever known, making never-before-seen advancements in architecture, medicine, civic organization, mathematics, philosophy, astronomy, and more.[7] While carving script onto stone walls between the 12th and 5th centuries BCE,[8] ancient Greeks displayed dual-dominance in their biscriptal writing style known as boustrophedon – a word that means, "Like the ox plowing at a turn."[9] Boustrophedon writing flows in one direction, then continues the next line in the opposite direction, creating mirrored script (see

CHAPTER 1

History's Spectrum of MMD

Nothing in the bilateral, mechanical design of the average human body can explain our overwhelming, global preference for developing the right hand over the left.[1] In fact, nearly all bilateral species under the sun have an even 50/50 split in handedness.[2] Humans are the only bilateral species with a drastic split – nearly 90% still favoring the right hand over the left. As a result, much of our human-designed world is asymmetric.[3] Everything from power tools to zippers and can openers are made exclusively for use by the right hand. This can explain how the left-handed must practice some mixed-handed degree of ambidexterity. If you need proof, grab a can of tuna and try using your left hand to open it.

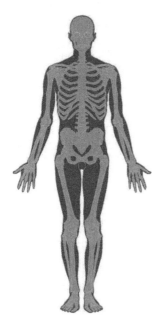

Figure 1.1: Humans are mechanically designed for symmetric movement

lifestyle to get there. BIG3MMD is dedicated to those up-and-coming MMD practitioners. While the stories of contemporary MMD practitioners merit writing a future book, let's first start with the stories of our historic, world-changing MMD practitioners...

macro 60
Major League Baseball 14
Mantle, Mickey 59
manual transfer learning 9, 40, 78
master 17, 21, 41
McCartney, Sir Paul 34
McManus, Chris 33
measuring cups 49
mechanical 3, 8, 11, 42, 71
mechanics 12, 23, 40-41, 60
medical oddities 17
Mellick, Chuck 61
memories 50, 58
memory 52, 57-58, 61, 68
mental 8-9, 46, 54, 68-69, 71
merit badges 27
meteorology 39
Michelangelo 2, 14, 16, 38
micro 40, 60
Microsoft 42
microwaves 49
military 13, 27
Mirror Read, Inc 68
mirror reading 1, 3, 33-35, 39, 43, 46, 53, 67-70
mirror script 1, 12, 18, 34, 37, 68
mirror therapy 53-54, 74
mirror writing 34, 37-39, 41-42, 49, 53, 68, 73
mirror-image 7, 21, 33, 42, 53-54, 68, 70
MirrorRead.com 68-69, 74
mirrors 41
mixed-handed 5, 11, 58

MMD 1, 3, 5, 7-11, 12-15, 20-21, 23, 26, 28, 31, 33, 35-37, 40, 42, 45-51, 53, 55, 57-66, 68-73, 75
MMD-trained body 64
mobility 54
Mogavero, Richard 73
Morris, Brad 74
motor strip 50-51
movement 3, 7, 9, 25, 42, 47-48, 53, 59, 63-65, 71
Mozart 14, 16
MRI 69
multilingual 17, 29
muscles 38, 40, 49-50
Mütter, Dr. Thomas Dent 17
myelination 61
myofascial linkages 64

native intelligence 20
naturephile 15, 36-37, 71-72
negative 46, 49
nervous system 61
neurogenesis 50, 52
neurological 51, 71
neurons 50-51, 69
neuroplasticity 50, 69
neuroscience 46, 50,
neurosurgeon 63
new movement ability 57
new neural development 62
Newell, Peter 18
New-England Courant 33
NHL 65-66
non-dominant 7
notebooks 13, 37, 40, 42, 49

citation lacking, please remember the words of my fellow MMD practitioner, the informally schooled, Leonardo da Vinci: "Though I may not, like them (the 'experts'), be able to quote other authors, I shall rely on that which is much greater and more worthy; on experience, the mistress of their Masters." *

My personal relationship with MMD began inadvertently 15 years ago as a way to physically rehabilitate my body from 10 years of skateboarding, which was done entirely using my dominant side. Frequent visits to chiropractors didn't solve my body alignment problems, so I reluctantly quit the sport. One year later, in 2007, I had the idea to try switch-stance skating. Switch-stance means performing the activity from your less-dominant side (aka mirrored). Up to this moment, I did everything in life exclusively right-handed and right-footed, so switching my stance was extremely challenging. I persisted though and guess what? This lifestyle practice notably realigned my body after just four years!

Shortly after, I returned to trying my regular stance in skateboarding again. I was quite nervous though as I did not want to reinjure myself. Surprisingly, I found that I was immediately able to perform new regular-stance tricks – thanks to a beautiful concept known as manual transfer learning.? I then wondered, "What would happen to my body if I learned everything switch?" From that moment, I gradually worked to learn everything switch-stance. This is the lifestyle practice of mirror movement development (MMD).

Today, after a cumulative 10+ years of practicing MMD, I started AmbiLife.org to introduce others to the lifestyle. MMD has not only astronomically changed my life, but also the lives of other practitioners I know.

There are people today reading this book who want to physically and mentally feel as good as I do and are willing to adopt the MMD

'less-dominant,' when referring to handedness and footedness in BIG3MMD. A 'non-dominant' hand leaves little room for improvement. However, a 'less-dominant' hand is open to improvement through practice over time.

In the same spirit, the word 'CAN'T' has no place within the vocabulary of an average person when it comes to MMD. If the average person says, "I can't write or throw with my other hand," an appropriate response would be, "Okay, what is your physical disability then?" After looking confused, they may follow up with, "Well, nothing. I just don't know how to use my other hand that well." Which is okay! You are correct to say that today, but fluency develops over time with practice. MMD is all about the practice of working to develop your less-dominant side to become the dual-dominant person you are mechanically designed to be.

While MMD is nothing new to humanity, our contemporary awareness of it is somewhat novel. Science today is developing a better understanding of MMD and how it benefits both the mind and body. While there is ample scientific citation throughout BIG3MMD, the practice of MMD merits greater research, considering the practice's highly-attractive benefits.[4] The goal of BIG3MMD is to present accounts of famous, historic MMD practitioners and an understanding of the science and benefits of the practice through which readers can get a glimpse into the reality that dual-dominance can be developed today by any average person.

First and foremost, my interest is to see people inspired to practice MMD and experience the mental and physical benefits. My credentials for writing BIG3MMD lie not in being a doctor, historian, professor, researcher, or other academic professional, but rather in the experience of being a 10+ year practitioner of MMD whose life has been dramatically changed by it. So, wherever you find

INTRODUCTION

Figure X.1 Average hands, like our bilateral sides, are mirror images

An ambidexter is someone who displays notable use of both hands, a trait commonly known as ambidexterity. The lives of many contemporary ambidexters show us that this skill is **not** something you are only born with, but can be developed through practice by any average person.[1]

Mirror movement development (MMD) focuses on choosing to use your less-dominant side in mirrored direction for all activities. This lifestyle practice produces dual-dominance. 'Dual-dominance,' is a more accurate term for the word 'ambidexterity,' which in Latin means, "right-handed on both sides,"[2] or "two rights."[3] Since humans have both left and right lateral sides, 'ambidexterity,' is not the most accurate word for describing the equal development of both mirrored sides of the human body. Cultures worldwide, though, have spent centuries understanding the practice of MMD as 'ambidexterity,' so this word is still used throughout BIG3MMD to describe dual-dominance, and vice versa.

One important part of the MMD lifestyle practice is having a Can-Do mindset of seeing our glasses as half-full. As a result, the commonly used word of 'non-dominant,' has been replaced with

DISCLAIMER

BIG3MMD came about after researching famous ambidextrous people from history. Various names appeared repeatedly in books and on websites. Those names and accounts are summarized here in BIG3MMD.

These famous people demonstrated a spectrum of handedness, from strongly mixed-handed – using different hands for different tasks (e.g. right-handed for tennis and left-handed for writing, like Bill Gates) – to highly ambidextrous. For many people, the word 'ambidextrous' has come to mean 'mixed-handed,' though the actual definition of ambidexterity means possessing an equal aptitude of either hand for all tasks. True ambidexterity has been quite rare, currently believed to be just one or two people in 1,000. Some scientists even argue that no one is entirely ambidextrous.[1]

It is even possible that some of these people were never ambidextrous at all, as in the cases of Albert Einstein and Benjamin Franklin – neither of whom ever wrote directly about their own handedness.[2] The people listed in BIG3MMD are all historic figures, so we cannot ask them today for clarification on their handedness. As a result, additional research and new information may produce another compelling edition of BIG3MMD in the future.

Regardless of the spectrum of BIG3MMD's historic ambidextrous, contemporary MMD practitioners show us that **ambidexterity (aka dual-dominance) can be developed by the average person through practice. Learn more at AmbiLife.org.**

5

WHAT IS MMD?

MMD is *mirror movement development*. Traditionally referred to as the practice of developing ambidexterity (aka dual-dominance), MMD is the mechanical design for optimal movement within our bilateral human body. It is practiced through focused development of the less-dominant side via mirrored movements. Examples of MMD include throwing with your less-dominant arm, kicking with your less-dominant foot, writing in mirrored direction with your less-dominant hand, reading in mirrored direction, and more.

The history, science, and benefits of MMD are presented here in BIG3MMD. The wide spectrum of historic ambidexters include three most notable: Lord Robert Baden-Powell, Benjamin Franklin, and Leonardo da Vinci. Additional information about MMD and stories from today's practitioners are available on my website, AmbiLife.org

HOW TO READ A BISCRIPTAL BOOK

BIG3MMD is the world's first modern biscriptal book. It is written in both traditional and mirrored script. To start the mirrored portion, simply flip the book over and begin at the 'back,' reading right-to-left. Both the traditional and mirrored versions include the same content. Your brain processes the mirrored version differently, though, growing your less-dominant brain hemisphere in the process.[1]

If you can read in the traditional direction, **mirror reading is achievable.** Like every new skill we learn, the ability to mirror read improves over time with practice. Remember, it took you time to learn reading in the traditional direction. Mirrored reading is no different. In fact, developmental studies show that cerebral symmetry is evident in children only before they learn traditional, unidirectional reading. This condition is balanced out through mirror reading and the general practice of MMD.[2]

Stick with this practice of mirror reading and your brain will thank you for the workout! You will learn more about the benefits of this exercise later in Chapter 5 on Mirror Reading.

TABLE OF CONTENTS

BIG3MMD

HISTORY'S AMBIDEXTROUS AND THE BENEFITS OF MIRROR MOVEMENT DEVELOPMENT

JIM HOULISTON

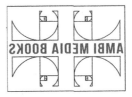

Written by Jim Houliston

Edited by Patricia Wallace
Editorial assistance by David Reisman, Richard Mogavero, and Maria Recupero English

Cover Image by J.P. Heston
Formatted by Saqib Arshad

ISBN: 979-8-986152-0-9 (Paperback)
Library of Congress Control Number: 2022908218

First printing, May 2022
Philadelphia, PA 19104

www.AmbiLife.org

BIG3MMD: History's Ambidextrous and the Benefits of Mirror Movement Development covers the history, science, and benefits of mirror movement development (MMD). It is the world's first modern bi-script book, written in both traditional and mirrored script.

Who are the "Big Three" in BIG3MMD? They are Leonardo da Vinci, Benjamin Franklin, and Lord Robert Baden-Powell — three of the most interesting, dual-dominant people of our millennium.

Dual-dominance — traditionally known as ambidexterity — can be developed by any average person through the practice of MMD for astounding benefits to both the body and brain.

Each of the historic MMD practitioners listed in BIG3MMD exercised and promoted dual-dominance as a springboard to greatness. For example, did you know that Michelangelo painted the Sistine Chapel with both hands? Or that Mozart composed music with the same approach? Even Houdini developed dual-dominance to become a better magician and encouraged the practice be taught to children!

Additional historic MMD practitioners and promoters include:

Ancient Greece	Plato	M.C. Escher
Thomas Jefferson	Hippocrates	Nikola Tesla
Mahatma Gandhi	Queen Victoria	Jimi Hendrix
James Garfield	Albert Einstein	Gordie Howe
Lewis Carroll	Easter Islanders	Mickey Mantle

The handedness of these historic figures, various of whom were polymaths, virtuosos, and renaissance men, is presented here in BIG3MMD.